Lavender & Peppermint Tea

Gentle Affirmations That Will Calm Your Mind and Ease Your Spirit as a New Nurse

Affirmations and Reflections by:
Jannel Gooden, BSN, RN

Inspired by real life experiences as a nurse

Contributions to affirmations by
Ashley Kennedy, MSN, RN

Print ISBN: 978-0-578-68134-4
E-book ISBN: 978-0-578-85161-7

Lavender & Peppermint Tea

This book is dedicated to my beautiful, hardworking mother, Pansy Williams.

For every hour you had to stand to give me this chance, thank you. For the opportunities you had to put down so I could one day pick them up, thank you. For loving me so very unconditionally, thank you. Your gentle and loving spirit was everything I needed to maneuver this lifetime. Mommy, you deserve all the accolades. And I promise to continue making you proud. I am honored God chose you to be my mother.

—*Your daughter, Jannel*

And to my grandparents and aunts and uncles and family friends who shared in holding me closely and providing a shelter of love for me as I blossomed into this woman, I thank you from the deepest parts of my heart. It took a village, and I am proud to have been a part of yours.

When God blesses you with an idea at 1 am in your sleep, you don't question it or second-guess it. You go with it. You let the idea carry you on its wings and you fly to heights intended just for you.

This book was written to encourage you through countless sleep-less nights with bloodshot eyes as you focus on tiny words in a textbook,

To help you look past everyone who has told you this was not possible,

For the many hours of critical thinking questions you reviewed until you no longer knew if you could trust your judgment,

For all the parties and quality time with friends and family that you missed out on,

For the vacations you could not afford,

For the interviewers who did not believe in you and for the ones who did,

For the strength to make it through the first year of nursing,

Welcome to *Lavender & Peppermint Tea...*

Foreword

PEPPERMINT TEA WAS A staple in my Jamaican household. Headache? Peppermint tea. Upset stomach? Peppermint tea. Unable to find the words to finish that book you've been staring at for months? Peppermint tea. You see, both lavender and peppermint tea provide a calmness, like no other, to my unsettled spirit. When life feels impossible and the day ahead seems too long to bear, I find my secret spot away from everything. I close the world out, put some water in my kettle, massage my body with oil and wait for my strength to return to me.

That is also how the title *Lavender & Peppermint Tea* came to me. Filled with angst about my deadlines for this book, insomnia crept into my bed insidiously. Lying awake one night with butterflies in my tummy, the title came to me divinely as I reached for my lavender essential oil. I doused my body with it in the hope that it would work just one more time to ease my mind. It has never failed me yet. With each deep breath I could feel my heart rate finally slowing down. I allowed the oils to marinate my skin and my thoughts began to melt away. It has always been the secret weapon against my anxiety. It never stands a chance.

I am hoping this book will become your lavender and peppermint tea; a small token of my love for you as a new nurse. This is a book of many gentle affirmations, but that is not all you will find here. I want you to find your truest nursing self. Who you are in difficult moments. How you cope as a nurse. How the process is affecting you. We go to school and spend years focused on the skills required to practice safely, but no one spends the time to nurture us through the heartache that is new nursing. What about the other skills needed to get through this grueling emotional process? No one tells us that some days we will feel defeated, or that some days we may want to quit. No one even tells us that quitting is our right if we are not flourishing. That taking a stand for yourself and quitting a job that is not suited to you is your prerogative and in no way reflects your abilities! No one tells us that our first job does not have to last 10 years or that we do not have to take our first job offers. No one tells us nursing has many different faces and styles and options; that not starting or ever working in the hospital is not a deal breaker. No one walks us through the steps of how to remain confident after that miserable physician rips us apart or how we pick our spirit up off the floor and make it through another day with that preceptor who just can't seem to remember how difficult it is to be new.

I want this to be your go-to book after a long day of work. Your lavender and peppermint tea. I want this to be your go-to book before you begin each shift. A way for you to reflect and organize your thoughts. This book is my way of helping you cope. So pause where it says pause. Reflect where it says reflect, and journal every honest feeling where prompted. Do not move on from an affirmation until you understand where it fits in your life. Sneak it into the bathroom if you need to vent. Write it out.

This book is your personal coach. I hope it will help you get through your days as a new nurse.

Metamorphosis

I understand that fear governs your practice right now.
But remember, on this journey, the darkness is necessary.
Gently affirm to yourself:

Like a caterpillar patiently awaiting
the growth of its wings,
so will I patiently endure this challenging
journey as a new nurse,
holding on to the promise that I too will one day
be a stunning butterfly who moves effort-
lessly in all situations.

HAVE YOU EVER BEEN in darkness? I don't mean an emotional or spiritual period of darkness. I mean real darkness. Like your lights are out in the middle of a storm or you forgot to pay your electricity bill so they cut that thang off before you get home darkness. It is the most awful experience ever. Take my word for it. After that first flip of the light switch with no response, you go through so many emotions before you actually come to your senses and accept that no light is coming through those bulbs anytime soon.

When I was in nursing school, I remember coming home one day to a pitch-black apartment and going into a complete panic.

First, because the lights were off and I knew I left them on because I'm a scaredy cat who always leaves a kitchen or hallway light on before I leave the house so I never have to come home to darkness. Second, because the light switch was giving me no light no matter how many times I flicked it. The first emotion I went through was denial. I flipped the switch on and off like crazy before I actually believed the lights were out. Then more denial as I moved to other light switches in the house because there was no possible way all the lights in the house were off. Welp! They were off. Then my fear set in. Oh damn! I've come home to a pitch-black apartment alone; what awaits me in this dark abyss? Is the boogie man out there? Did someone cut the circuit breaker and is now waiting to kidnap me? I clearly watch too many horror movies. The panic flooded my body and I was frozen. Then logic quickly took over and I searched for some hope. I started looking around for a candle or a flashlight. I ended up using the light on my phone to guide me around the house. But the light wasn't that bright. I could only see a few inches in front of me. I was still scared. I didn't really want to be in the house, but I realized that walking through that period of darkness was necessary for me to function through the night.

Now here comes my magical metaphor that will tie this story together and help you understand my point in sharing it. Waiting in the darkness sucks! It's painful. It triggers all your worst fears! Every insecurity you've ever had sits on your chest and weighs you down. The darkness is awful, until you embrace the idea that it is necessary for you to go through it if you want to make it to the light. Sure, I could have sat in the dark apartment and cried my little eyes out, but I had things that needed to be done. Lying down and quitting on life wasn't a viable option. How does one embrace the glory that is a full and complete life without going through the hardest times that groom you to be fit for those magical moments when they arrive? The darkness gives you grit. It teaches you strength. You learn resilience when you come out on the other side. If I never walked into an apartment of darkness a couple times in my life, I may have never learned the discipline of having a budget and paying those bills on time. Had I never felt that fear of the darkness, would I ever have known why it's so important to always have a flashlight with batteries in every room in the house? The darkness is your teacher, if you let it be. Don't spend the dark hours complaining; you should be strategizing and preparing. Asking yourself, what am I supposed to be paying attention to right now? The wait is the worst part. Like waiting for the electrical company to open up so you can pay the bill to have lights again. The wait feels like some of the darkest times of our lives, but it proves to be a very necessary teacher. The caterpillar's wait has to be the most difficult part in the journey to becoming a butterfly, but it can't be avoided. You can't be a butterfly without first being a caterpillar. Google the process. It's dark, it's lonely, but they never give up because they trust the process. They have no idea what's ahead, but they trust their journey.

I wonder how many of us would still sign up for this journey of nursing if we truly got a glimpse of the stress ahead. If the butterfly doesn't trust the process and push forward, it dies. Its dreams and aspirations to one day be lifted high above the ground and have the gift of flight dies with it.

Your journey will be the same. The moments when you are just trying to make it to lunch time so you can sit down for a second will prove to be the most difficult. You will have the hardest time trying to understand the purpose in the process. But I need you to realize that those are the moments that shape your discipline. That is where you will find your determination. It's in those moments that you will learn how to keep pushing for that patient who is decompensating and needs your full attention and focus, even though you have not had even a sip of water in hours. It's in those moments of difficulty where you will learn to selflessly put your patients first, that will teach you how to soothe the cries of a family member mourning the passing of their loved one, even though you may be mourning your own losses. It's those moments that will give you the courage to approach anyone in your way if it means advocating for the wellbeing of those entrusted in your care.

So yes, it may feel terrible now. No, you can't understand it all today. But one day, those wings will blossom from your cocoon and you will transform right before your own eyes. You'll bloom and make yourself proud. But for now, change your relationship with the darkness. Love the darkness. Don't resent it. A butterfly is a caterpillar who didn't resent the process.

I am a good nurse

While the darkness is necessary, remember that it is also temporary.

So on the days where you feel like you cannot go on, gently affirm to yourself:

I am not timid.
I am just not comfortable.
I am still gaining my experience.
But just as the sky holds on to the prom-
ise of the sun returning in the morning,
I too will understand that these moments
of darkness I feel as a new nurse
are only temporary.

I REMEMBER FEELING JUST plain stupid as a new grad nurse. I had to Google everything. When a doctor would walk into the room explaining some complex plan of care to my patient, I would feel the resentment growing in me, as I knew I would be left explaining something to my patient that I barely understood myself. Because no patient will ever just ask the doctor what the heck they are talking about! No, they'll wait until the doctor leaves and expect the nurse to explain it all to them again, and this time in English. (Insert eye roll!) Which, of course, we should be able to, but at that stage I didn't understand everything yet.

A lot of what I had to deal with was completely new—we never even discussed most of those things in nursing school!—and I hated that I didn't know it all. Most concepts were coming at me so fast that I would nod my head in agreement, but deep down inside I was making a mental note to revisit the topic later. To avoid any embarrassment, I would never dare interrupt my preceptor with my silly questions. I could not stand the look of disappointment that would appear on a colleague's face when I asked a question they felt I should know the answers to. Come on sis, I forgot what that means, just explain it to me without all the shaming involved. Experienced nurses don't realize that it takes a lot of courage for a new nurse to ask questions after a certain point post orientation. Initially, any question is a good question. But after a couple of months to a year, you start to feel a little embarrassed about the things you don't remember.

So I learned to use coping mechanisms. I learned them fast to appear competent and stay ahead of the learning curve. I learned to ask my questions more eloquently so I could hide the real confusion that was deeply rooted in them. I also learned to sneakily rotate my questions, directing them at everyone on the unit, taking turns so no one person would think I was stupid and asking too many questions. God forbid they had a pow wow about me and realized how many questions I was actually asking! I learned to nod yes now and Google later. This situation was really unpleasant, not to mention unfair to me as the new nurse and to my patients. None of it truly made sense in the moment. I was just hoping that one day it would all magically come together. I felt like a child. Trying to put together what was concrete and visible to the eye, not always realizing there was a deeper and more complex meaning taking place. Like a patient being short of breath and me not realizing they may need some Lasix. It was too much and too soon for me to get that. It was rough. Most days I wondered why I was even hired or how I managed to pass a state board.

You can forget the idea that a magic wand of understanding is going to sweep over your head after passing boards and completing orientation. It takes true hard work for everything to start making sense. I had to learn to speak more kindly to myself. I had to stop comparing myself to others. Trust me, my comparison game was by no means fair. I would compare my eight months of skills to those of a 15-year nursing vet. I remember looking at nurses who had been on my unit for some time with so much envy growing in my heart. Envious of their flow. Envious at how things came so easy to them. Envious at all the respect the doctors had for their opinions. I felt so discouraged. I didn't recognize that those nurses were also once new and that they also, once upon a time, experienced their own periods of darkness. I wasn't accepting that my moments were only temporary and one day would be in the distant past. I couldn't grasp that I wouldn't always feel like that.

It's easy to feel discouraged when everyone around you is flourishing. I had to come to the realization that although I was smart, I was growing in a new field, and that can make you feel really stupid in a room full of people who have been doing something for a long time. Nursing is not like an art degree. No one dies if you stroke your brush in the wrong direction. I had to accept that time would enhance the hard work I was already putting in. Learning to acknowledge those moments of struggle and doubt as temporary was vital to my self-esteem, because when you're knee deep in it, it feels like forever. When we can see that moments are just that, moments, we won't feel as trapped in them. It's totally acceptable to be a bit nervous today. It's ok that your movements appear timid. There's nothing wrong with all that discomfort. You are growing and gaining experience, and this lack of confidence is only temporary.

The night sky enjoys the moon and the stars. It realizes it is part of a cycle and understands the sun will eventually come out. The sun knows without a doubt that its time will come to shine. Remember the same for yourself. This too, without a doubt, shall pass.

Confidence

When you think being a great nurse means having a great day, gently affirm to yourself:

I vow to love myself as a nurse without conditions. I am not a great nurse because my day went perfectly. I am a great nurse because I got up today and gave it my all. I am a great nurse even when chaos and confusion was the theme of my day.

MY CONFIDENCE AS A new nurse was very conditional. It stood on such shaky ground. It vacillated with every changing circumstance, and as you can imagine, change is constant in an acute care setting. My confidence swayed with every change. If you asked me how confident I was feeling in the morning and again later in the evening, you'd get two totally different answers. I was so unsure of myself, and I could feel my uncertainty with every changing moment. I hated it. My feelings swayed with each changing circumstance, and I felt like I had no consistent feelings about myself that I could rely on. I allowed everything around me to dictate my emotions.

I also had a lot of conditions in place for my confidence as a new nurse, which doesn't help the already elusive concept of confidence when you're new! If I left work on time, I was happy and confident.

If the next day I was late with a med, I would completely forget the amazing shift I had the day before and stick myself in the dog house. I was emotionally exhausted, and I know you are emotionally exhausted too because you probably do the same. "If I get all my work done by change of shift with nothing to delegate, all my patients are happy and everyone thanks me for my help today, it means I'm a great nurse." This is the crap we feed ourselves. That our self-worth as a nurse is determined by our perfection. The sort of perfection we aspire to is very rarely achieved, if ever, and especially not in the beginning of our careers. This leaves us with a chronic feeling of incompetency. We hold ourselves up to very unfair standards. We have too many conditions in place and too many fluctuating emotions. We're never above the swinging pendulum.

Have you ever heard of the law of attraction? Well, amongst the many universal laws that exist is the law of rhythm. In its simplicity, it states that the energy of the universe is always swaying, moving, and flowing. It is continuously moving from left to right, like a pendulum. Universal energy is always moving between two opposites on a continuum, for example, being very happy versus being incredibly sad. The thing is, life will always throw circumstances at you that can either bring you really high or really low. The key is to control our emotions in these moments. Did you ever play a video or board game with a child? If they win in round one, they bounce around happy and excited, but if they begin to lose in round two, they fuss and cry and become bratty. Now think about yourself in such moments. Your experience has taught you that winning or losing a game means nothing in the grand scheme of things, so you're neither very excited if you win or very sad if you lose. You're just relaxed and happy to be spending time with this kid who is probably losing their mind when things don't go their way. They haven't built up enough life skills to not be so reactive to changing circumstances.

Just realize for a second that we do this in our real lives too. We allow our emotions to swing with the pendulum of life. We don't remain poised in our daily lives the way we do in the game. We forget that you win some and you lose some, and either way, you're going to be fine. No, we completely abandon that sense of calm, and we feel an obligation to the emotions that arise. We get pulled away from our balance. It takes a lot of practice and self-awareness to remain balanced and above the swinging pendulum. Ideally, if you had a great day, you shouldn't get overly excited, and if the day was really challenging, you shouldn't get depressed. You should stay at a peaceful medium regardless of the circumstances of your shift and day. This is how you accomplish true peace and fulfillment at work. Nothing should sway you into over-confidence, and nothing should be able to pull you into deep depression. In every moment, you should remain in a constant state of balance, knowing that no bad moment will last for the duration of your career, or even for the week.

This is how you begin to love your nursing self. This is how you remain confident as a new nurse. You place no conditions on your confidence. You stay balanced in your feelings about your abilities. You remove the conditions. If it's a great day, you're confident that you did your best. If it's a challenging day where everything went wrong, you acknowledge the difficulty in the day, but you remain confident in your ability to improve. We place so many conditions on our life, it's no wonder we believe that an easy, seamless day equates to being a bomb nurse. Listen Linda! You're in the wrong profession if you're expecting breakfast in bed every shift. You must remember, you're a great nurse even when your patient codes. You're a great nurse even when your patient complains.

Who you are as a nurse is not dependent on the outcome of your day. When you do your best at all times, you are a great nurse. It's really that simple. You only have the capacity to operate from what you know to be true and best. So you made an honest mistake? You are still a great nurse. I know it's tempting to judge yourself by how you feel at the end of the shift, but that isn't always the most accurate scale. Give yourself grace. Give yourself some wiggle room. Change your mindset and the conditions you have in place, and you'll change your relationship with your work self-esteem.

Balance

One the days where the instability of being new is getting the best of you,
gently affirm to yourself:

Your first year of nursing is like riding a bike.
Everything feels impossible without your training wheels (your preceptor).
It's really difficult to find your balance (your time management).
You may fall down some days and get some cuts and bruises (your mistakes),
But with time and patience you will learn the rhythm (your daily routine).
Every day will not be sunny.
You will need to learn how to pedal through different seasons,
BUT with practice and patience you'll be cruising in no time!

I REMEMBER A WEEK I had in PICU that perfectly exemplifies the swinging pendulum and the instability of our days and emotions as new nurses. The Chief Nursing Officer of the hospital came up to me to personally let me know that she'd heard so many good things about my performance on the floor and she wanted to let me know how proud she was to have me on her team. I was like, damn, look at this lil' girl from the Bronx having the CNO come up to her telling her how amazing she was. I was proud! I literally bragged to everyone about the compliment I was given. But in that same week, a family accused me of negligent behavior. WTF! I had just gotten this incredible compliment from my director in my first year as a nurse, and now I was being accused of the most unthinkable, most neglectful thing you could ever think of, all in the same week. I was torn up to say the least, and embarrassed and worried that my CNO would think less of me. The same family member also accused me of a whole host of other negligent behaviors. Things that made no sense because I had the documentation to back me up and witnesses on my side. I am very OCD at the bedside, so none of the claims made sense to me or anyone who had ever worked with me up until that point. Still, the accusations hurt me. I was so down. I felt like I had to jump through hoops to vindicate myself. Needless to say, it didn't take any more accusations before we all decided I needed to not care for this patient anymore. I was hurt. I was tearful for days after my shift. Why? Not because I did anything wrong—my documentation and account of each situation and this family's irrational behavior with other nurses proved me right— but because it made me second-guess myself as a nurse. Even though the CNO reassured me that they fully investigated the situation and she still thought I was amazing and had nothing to worry about, I still felt like my reputation was ruined. I was so fragile then. Thinking back to that situation now I can only laugh, knowing that my present self wouldn't even bat an eye at that level of crazy from a patient's family. Because I know myself now. I'm not sitting around allowing situations to define me. The instability of the circumstances around me no longer cause me to lose my balance with it.

You see, the thing about low confidence is that you can be tormented even by a blatant lie about yourself. You have no roots in the ground, so any breeze can blow you over. You know your truth but you don't fully embody it as a great nurse, so it feels like someone could show up at any given moment and prove you to be the awful nurse you suspected you were all along. In those early days, I wanted to cry and quit every time I faced a hiccup. I allowed changing conditions to dictate my confidence. I had to lay in my pool of tears many more times over the next couple of months over other situations before I realized they didn't define my character. They didn't define my nursing abilities or the effort I put into my patients. A pissed-off family member didn't make me a bad nurse. A physician having a bad day screaming rude comments at me didn't make me a bad nurse. I was a great freaking nurse, doing my best during every single shift, yet I allowed some moments to make me feel defeated. I didn't realize how erratic these emotions were until I started becoming aware of how happy a compliment would make me and how down I would get with critique. I was making myself crazy, and for what? Up and down constantly. Back and forth. Some days I was good, other days I was a disaster. I needed to find my peace at the bedside. I deserved my peace, and so do you!

I made up my mind that I wasn't going to allow anything to shake me anymore. I deserved more than to become my emotions. I deserved more for myself than to allow external circumstances to dictate my level of confidence. I found my peace, and I trust that you will soon find yours too. Take your power back. Stop giving it away to those who don't deserve that kind of authority over your career and life.

Activity: Create a vision board

Are you familiar with a vision board?

Have you ever created one?

What about one specifically for your nursing goals and aspirations?

What we constantly think and obsess over in our minds and speak with our mouths manifest our physical experiences. What we actively work towards has no other choice but to show up in our lives. This is why it is so important to be intentional in everything we do. All the little nagging thoughts of defeat will begin to appear in your work life if you continue to give them space to grow in your mind.

Living with intention means carefully choosing your words. The ones you speak to yourself and to others. It means only taking part in activities that move you closer to where you see yourself. Not a fan of a particular group of people at work because they are constantly gossiping? Then remove yourself from the conversation if you don't want to be the next gossip girl or guy on your unit. Everything you do daily, whether consciously or subconsciously will contribute to your rise or your fall. So why not partake in activities that are meaningful, powerful, and transformational?

A great way to aid your intentional living is to create a vision board. A vision board acts as a guide to remind you what you are working towards. It is a way to visualize your biggest goals; a way to see and think about them every day! As a result, you will keep working towards them. Vision boards are a powerful tool for executing. Your vision board helps to accelerate the desires of your heart by forcing you to move them from your imagination to a more tangible place. Any and everything can be placed on your nursing vision board. Want to become an advanced practice registered nurse? Place the exact title of your dream role with your full name on your board. Want to work in a particular hospital on a particular floor? Find pictures of that hospital and place it on your vision board. That's exactly what I did when I wanted a contract at a particular hospital that was never open to travel nursing. I got that job and stayed there for multiple contracts. Want to just feel more confident? Use specific words to describe your confidence and place them directly on your board. Get as detailed as possible about where you see your nursing self.

Start by closing your eyes and envisioning how good reaching your goals will feel. Start feeling the tingles in your body. You will feel yourself start walking into your full purpose.

Something incredible happens when you start envisioning yourself in the way you want to be. Your environment starts shifting to help you manifest. You begin to move in alignment with everything you are requesting. A vision board brings to life the things you keep in the back of your mind in a way that reminds you to keep pressing towards them. All things in our physical realm start with a simple thought process that we nurture into reality.

Now it's your turn. Use the space that follows to write down all your nursing goals, whether they're big or small. Simple or detailed. Anything and everything you want for yourself now and in the future should be written down here. Then go and create a vision board that reflects these goals in written and picture form. Place that vision board in plain sight. Review your vision board every day and speak your vision out loud. Start creating a plan to accomplish each thing. Work at that plan day in and day out. Believe in its possibility. Then watch mountains start moving in your favor.

There is a pattern here. Have you caught it? We write things down. Bringing things out of your mind and onto paper creates a magnetic effect! You'll see it every day! You'll keep it on your mind. It never leaves you. Eventually, you'll pull it into your physical experience.

_____

_____

_____

_____

_____

_____

_____

_____

_____

_____

_____

_____

_____

_____

_____

Affirmation

Repeat after me:

I have autonomy over my career path.
I make decisions daily that set me up for a winning season.
I speak my desires into reality.
I co-create with the infinite power that
is to bring forth my best life.

We all make mistakes

On the days your mistakes get the best of you,
gently affirm to yourself:

I will accept that every mistake is not defeat.
What I learn from my mistakes
are the most valuable parts of my nursing journey.

Be gentle with yourself.

Be
gentle
with
yourself!

MISTAKES ARE EMBARRASSING. LET'S face it. Even if they aren't run and
hide under the pillow worthy, they still have a little sting to them.
They can weigh heavily on you, depending on your relationship
with mistakes. How were your mistakes met as a child? What did
your family do when you made one? Was it a big messy ordeal?
Or were they met with compassion and understanding? I used to
never forget my mistakes. Needless to say how my mistakes were

met as a child. I would take them home with me. Out to dinner on the weekends. Tuck them into bed with me at night. I imagine you sometimes do the same.

I want you to stop this self-deprecating behavior and learn to forgive yourself. Release your mistakes. Reliving those moments over and over again will do nothing for you or your self-esteem. If you allow them to, they will damage your confidence. You will start obsessively checking and rechecking every little thing and that alone feels demoralizing. Replaying a mistake over and over will destroy your ability to intervene for your patient in a timely manner because you'll be afraid to screw up. And truth be told, the screw ups are the most meaningful parts of the journey. It's the meat of it all. It's the moment where theory meets practice and you learn the right way to go about that thing you've been dancing around. It creates a level of certainty. Welp, I guess I should hold down the other side of the port on this G-tube if I don't want all the meds to come splashing back at my face. It's how we all learn.

It takes willpower to rebound from a mistake. To be able to understand and respect its occurrence as a necessity for your growth. I am so incredibly grateful for every mistake I have ever made, and I want you to adopt the same gratitude. I am grateful because my mistakes revealed my weaknesses to me, presenting me with an opportunity to improve in those areas. Although I don't make many anymore because I am now more in tune with where I need help and self-assured about what I know, every mistake has brought me to this place. If you embrace your mistakes, they will lead you to a place of growth beyond what you think you are capable of. That's the miracle that comes with using your mistakes to your benefit.

But first, learn to forgive yourself, because the world isn't always that forgiving. It's an obligation you need to have to yourself to be gentle with your process. Because no one else owes you that. I remember this little phrase that used to grind my gears as a new nurse: "breaking my patient." Some nurses would jokingly ask other nurses whose shifts were awful and their patients decompensating if they broke the patient. I was asked this question a few times as a new nurse. I wanted to shout from a mountain top: SHUT UP! It's hard enough when you make a mistake, and it's even worse when those mistakes affect your patients' outcomes. It feels like death when someone pokes fun at it. It is a form of death for your self-esteem. It starts chipping away until you can barely muster the emotional strength for another shift. Our profession has made a culture out of crucifying those who make mistakes. As though our humanity doesn't factor in every now and then.

I want you to grow stronger and more confident. A big part of that is using your mistakes as a chance to pivot. Your chance to become more efficient. So don't run from them. Don't dig a hole and bury them, but definitely don't invite them out with you for Sunday brunch. Remember, mistakes offer an opportunity to grow and become more knowledgeable. So accept them head-on, figure out how you can improve, and do the research to fully understand how to avoid the mistake in future. But don't let them make you feel defeated ever again. Don't give them permission to eat away at you. Unless you've been a nurse in some past life, this is your first taste of nursing. You're not going to always get it right. No shame in that. Root those feet in the ground and pin your shoulders back. Mistakes are not the end of the road, they are the fork in the road. Will you choose the path that breaks your spirit and discourages you from the profession you worked so hard to be a part of? Or will you walk poised down the path that empowers you to keep growing and learning? Your choice.

Trust your intuition

When the physician asks why, but you have no concrete answer, gently affirm to yourself:

I will trust my gut today.
Even though I have no
explanation as to why I feel this way.
I will trust my gut anyway. Knowing that it speaks the secrets
of my patients.
A language only I as the nurse will understand.

Pause and let that truth sink in.
My gut speaks the secrets of my patients. A language only I as
the nurse will understand.

TRUSTING YOUR INTUITION AS a new nurse might be harder than trusting a partner after they cheated. In fact, trusting a cheating partner is a walk in the park compared to trusting what feels like a random thought with no real proof that it is valid. Especially with the added burden of having to share that thought with a more experienced nurse to get rid of the nagging in your head! The thing is, your intuition is a muscle that needs to be exercised. If you don't use it daily, you will never know its value.

One day during my orientation, I was listening to my patient's lungs and I thought I heard crackles. The longer I listened, the more confident I felt about what I heard. I quickly skipped to my preceptor to tell her what I had discovered. Naturally, I felt very proud of myself because up until this point I hadn't heard or seen anything she didn't discover first. Knowing that my reassessment had yielded a finding, I was ready to give myself the praise I expected her to give me. But with a skeptical look on her face, she decided to join me in the patient's room to hear for herself. She listened and decided he was clear. I was stunned because I knew I had heard those crackles and I listened long and hard. So, I insisted that she listen again. Very bold of me, considering how afraid of her I was at this point. She appeased my request and listened again, but insisted the patient was clear. For some reason, I was not convinced she was right on this day. I persisted and asked her to please listen again. She listened, and still, nothing. She then called a colleague in and asked their opinion. At this point, I just knew she was going to make an example out of my stupidity. I felt my confidence level draining with every second I stood there waiting for the other nurse to tell us she heard nothing. But this day! Chile, this day was different. The other nurse listened, and sure enough; crackles! I almost started break dancing from excitement! It was less about being right and more about me trusting what I had heard. Ok, at this point, it was about both. I was right, damnit, and you were wrong. I held on tightly to my professional opinion even when opposed by a more experienced nurse. Her initial assessment could have trumped mine, but I trusted myself.

When I first started going to spin class, I had a really hard time overcoming the resistance of the bike. It took me going back consistently to see that the resistance became easier to push through once my legs got stronger. As a new nurse, I had many days where I had no clue what was really wrong with my patients when they took a turn for the worse. It took so much practice for me to overcome the resistance in my mind that was telling me to ignore what I thought I saw. Couple that with sharing your thoughts with someone who is totally denying your reality, and well, it can make you feel a bit crazy and like you'll never get it right. I had to practice pushing through the doubt if I wanted to have any chance of being an intuitive nurse who trusted herself. The more you ignore your intuition, the quieter it gets, but the more you acknowledge it, the louder and more trustworthy it becomes. Your sixth sense is a great reason to alert someone else who you trust when you feel like something might be wrong. Call your charge nurse for a second opinion. Have someone talk you through what you are seeing, but be careful not to allow someone to talk you out of escalating care that you feel is necessary. Always consult a more experienced nurse when feeling uncertain. And if all else fails and neither of you have the answers, still page or call the doctor and let them know your concerns. But still try to gather some objective data before you approach the physician. While the sixth sense is understood in nursing, you need a more objective approach for your physician. You need facts and not feelings. You need assessments, lab work, and vital signs that support that idea you have in your mind. In a case like mine, look at ins and outs. Is the patient fluid overloaded? How is the patient's heart? Are crackles truly a possibility? Get that other nurse in to look and feel with you. Just know, where the sixth sense speaks, objectivity looms close by. You just need to find it. Be a detective and find anything that can give you another piece of the missing puzzle.

Sometimes your intuition speaks in smaller ways, like nudging you to go recheck that IV pump or that blood pressure.

You honestly have an obligation to your patient to find the objective data that supports your feelings. And still, when no one agrees with you or sees what you see, keep silently monitoring for any subtle changes. Because that's your job! That's the oath you took! The unspoken oath anyway, because I don't think I ever said an oath out loud. You vowed to be your patient's advocate, and that starts with knowing your stuff and trusting yourself. You can't speak up for others when you don't believe what you will say even matters. Every day you show up for a shift is a chance to become a better patient advocate.

That means assessing your patient again and again. Reassessing one more time. Really analyzing what you hear or see. Recommending labs be drawn or checked. Do you know how many times I've seen one or two PVCs on a monitor on my cardiac patient that wouldn't show when I had the physician standing there? Do you know how many times I had to trust my gut and advocate for a chemistry to be drawn so we could be absolutely certain no electrolytes needed to be replaced? Do you know how many "no they are fine, not right now's" I got? How many times I've been right and did a whole dance in my head because I followed my gut?

Always do what you think is right. Question doctors. Respectfully and professionally of course, but ask for an explanation when they refuse you. Let them stumble and stutter and agree to put in orders at your request. I don't know about you, but I sleep really well at night knowing that I double- and triple-checked something. It's not so easy to sleep at night with too many what if's swirling around your brain.

Everyone won't agree with your professional opinion, and that's fine. But who sat and took that licensing exam? Who paid that fee for that license and got their little fingerprints taken? Right. So at some point in your process, you must learn to trust yourself. Because if you are the first to respond to an emergency, the only opinion that matters will be yours. When everyone is busy and you need to make a split-second decision, what you gon' do? I'm at the point in my career now where I won't even document what someone else says without me seeing it with my own two eyes. No, sorry, I know you're running behind to clock out, but I didn't see that patient's bottom, so no ma'am, I'm not documenting skin intact. It's easy when you're new to get suckered into doing something you aren't comfortable with, but saying no is also a form of trust and integrity for yourself.

Start exercising that trust muscle. Your professional opinion matters just as much as anyone else's. The goal is for all our opinions to align, but when they don't, trust what you see and hear. Go up the chain of command when you feel overlooked. No hoop is too big to jump through when advocating for someone's life.

Intuition should not be confused with anxiety. Anxiety will have you doing and redoing with no real rhyme or reason. Practicing your skills and understanding your patient population will help you discern between anxiety and intuition. When you've been studying and trying to gain a true understanding of your specialty, you'll grow stronger in your advocacy and you will find the words that feel missing today. In the meantime, listen to the whispers inside of you and stay in tune with its frequency. Use your resources. Pass your concerns along to the oncoming nurse to monitor. Maybe you have no suggestions for the doctor; maybe it's just a matter of mentioning what you've noticed to them and they'll make the suggestions.

You know the worst thing a new nurse can do? Look at the previous nurse's assessment before they document their own.

It will dissuade you from believing your own judgment. Also, remember that things can change from shift to shift. If you're concerned with accuracy, looking at the previous nurse's charting won't bring you any closer than doubting yourself will. Don't make reviewing another nurse's charting your crutch. Learn to distinguish your own assessment skills from other nurses'. Keep reading up on your specialty. Keep practicing those skills. Taking action every day is how you learn to trust yourself as you journey along this windy road of new nursing. The only way to become more self-assured in your assessment skills is by actually doing it so you can put the theory to the test with real life experiences.

You're with your patient 12 hours in a day; sometimes multiple 12-hour shifts over a couple of days. Never be afraid to trust your intuitive nature. Never be afraid to take it up a notch in advocating for your patient's life. Think about it this way. You only tell your secrets to the people who are closest to you and you spend the most time with. Your patients feel the same way about you. We spend a lot of intimate time with them, so trust and believe you will be the first to know their bodies' little secrets.

Expert nurses rely on their intuition because they have an arsenal of experiences to guide them. You know how those experiences are able to guide them? Because they trusted everything they saw and did for themselves and their patients along the way. So go do more. Go see more. Go read more. And go trust yourself more with each step you take.

Here's the thing. When you are working with your team they don't have time to check your track record. They aren't there to check your latest report card. They are looking at your body language. They are listening to the tone of your voice. They are watching how you respond to the chaos. Those are ways that others know they can trust you. They need to feel your knowledge as much as they can hear you speak to them. This is the same confidence your patients crave from you. They are in the most desperate situations of their lives. They can't get a background check. They gauge your competence through ways you wouldn't initially realize. So go ahead and exude that air of confidence. Tell them all you know with your chin up and shoulders back. Because yes, your patients are judging you, the doctors are judging you, your peers are judging you. So give them something good to look at!

No one's perfect

On the days where you feel like you should have it all together by now,
gently affirm to yourself:

> I will remember
> that I am not supposed to know everything,
> even though being a new nurse
> makes me feel like I am supposed to.
> I will remember that "I am not sure"
> is an acceptable response and that
> every day is a chance to add something new to my
> memory bank.

DO YOU SUFFER FROM that infamous disease all nurses suffer from? What disease, you ask? The most self-limiting disease for a new nurse. Perfectionism. Why is this even a discussion? Because we're still killing ourselves every shift for a ticket to this imaginary destination. Some of us even want a first-class seat. You're not alone on that waiting list. The idea of perfection gives us anxiety. Because I don't know about you, but I'd be pretty damn frustrated if I set out on a road trip to a place that doesn't exist. Who do you ask for directions? When do you stop trying to find it? Perfection is something I still struggle with too, learning to let go of the idea that even after a great shift, somehow perfect would be attainable for me if I try harder tomorrow. But what is better than your best? I'll wait.

You cannot be a perfect nurse. Perfect folks only exist in the imagination. You will make mistakes. You will lose your rhythm. You cannot grow while claiming to be perfect. If you think everything should be perfect, you remove the idea that there are things you need to improve on. And we all know there is always something to improve on.

Something magical happens when you are willing to acknowledge your limitations. You stop feeling like you need to show up in the world as perfect. You accept your limitations as a part of your beautiful design, and they no longer haunt you. It's called surrender. You begin to surrender to your human nature. Surrender helps keep you humble. It reminds you that you can't do it all and healthcare wasn't designed for you to do it all.

This is why we have interdisciplinary teams and coworkers. It's why we delegate tasks. It's why everyone contributes a piece to the puzzle. You're only as good as your team members' attention to detail. That's why I can't do the doctor's job, and the doctor sure can't do mine.

You're a human being. Capable of mistakes. You get tired sometimes. You won't have all the answers. Contrary to what the lack of staffing laws would have you believe, you actually do need a break to recharge and reset. There is nothing perfect about even the most seemingly perfect nurse you've ever met. We all have our strengths and we all have our weaknesses. What I'm great at, you may suck at. If you want to test that theory, watch the nurses who float to your specialty. They are a fish out of water. They don't get what you do with ease because this is what you do every day, not them.

I think all nurses have a slight obsession with perfection. Unless you work in the ED! Then perfection is a foreign language you care nothing about! The thing is, we should all try to adopt that attitude in some way. This easygoing but efficient way of approaching our shift. That's not to say you should be negligent of course, but you should understand that perfection is a false narrative you keep feeding yourself. It's fake. A fairy tale. It does not exist. ED nurses are some of the best out there with no desire to achieve perfection because they understand their job in true depth. Stabilize and transfer out.

My obsession with perfection was even worse as a new nurse. Everything needed to be perfect or it would reflect my incompetence. That is what I thought, anyway. Damn it, I didn't say the right words with that effortless flow to the physician the way I envisioned I would, now I must waste time replaying it over and over taking up mental space in my head, letting it bug me all day and night. Did you get the point across Jannel? Good. Let it go and move on. Nope. I wanted to torture myself because I couldn't say it all perfectly. I had this insane desire to do everything right all the time, even if I hadn't done it before. I thought I needed to have an answer for everything, not realizing that not knowing and humbly accepting that I did not know was a way for me to gain insight on that particular topic. We feel so much pressure to have all the answers. To know all the details. This is where the desire to be perfect becomes toxic; when it becomes directly linked to our professional identities. We stop striving for our best, and we start aiming for perfect because anything less than, this fake place we're never getting to, feels like a failure. Imagine trying to go somewhere every day that you're never going to get to. Just imagine the full-on delusion in attempting to go somewhere that literally does not exist. So of course it feels like a failure. And of course we hate failures, and because we've attached our professional identity to this thing we can't attain, we now feel like our life as new nurses is failing too.

I worked with a "perfect" nurse once. She literally did no wrong. At least not in front of me. I felt like she knew everything. She executed all her tasks so beautifully. I tried comparing myself to her once, then I stopped in the first minute because it was too painful to try living up to her perfection. Then, one day, she knocked herself off her own pedestal by asking me a question. I won't even reveal the question because the answer was so simple to me, but she had no idea what the hell the doctor was asking her to do. She mentioned it to me as though I wouldn't know either, but I knew. I knew what the doctor was talking about, but Miss Perfect did not? This showed me really early on in my career that no one is perfect.

A wonderful nurse I used to work with, who was also seemingly perfect, once told me that a wise nurse doesn't know all the answers but knows where to *find* all the answers. This was a game changer for me! Your insecurities will mislead you into thinking you should have all the answers. This is a false perception of what it means to be a great nurse and it's simply not possible at this stage in your career. You should be striving for progress, not perfection. Building on what you did yesterday, not trying to outdo yesterday's performance. Every day is a new scenario. Even once you have enough knowledge under your belt after a few years, something else will sneak up and test you again. I still get diagnoses at work that I need to research. All these years in and some questions still give me the WTF face.

Practice only guarantees your progress, never perfection. Perfection is an elusive goal. If you set the bar at an unattainable height, you'll always feel inadequate, especially as a new nurse. The only thing you owe yourself is to improve every day. To make an effort to try harder at the things that feel challenging. Perfection can never be the goal because your idea of perfection will always change. When I was a new grad nurse, I just wanted to successfully place an IV. In my mind, that would feel have felt pretty damn perfect. Then, when I managed to successfully place an IV, I wanted to do so without my patient bleeding out everywhere in the process. I wanted my hands to relax and feel comfortable. Perfect changed to getting it without making a mess. Then I wanted to get it and not make a mess AND tape it perfectly. And on and on the story goes until here we are years later, and it still doesn't feel perfect because now I want all that and all the difficult sticks. Perfection will have you out there never clapping for yourself. Perfection will dampen the moments you should be celebrating yourself in.

Sometimes my IV dressings are ugly and sometimes the placement is a bloody mess. But those trivial things don't bug me anymore. I placed the IV. The patient got the Morphine. Check and check. It's not on my radar how perfect it looked. Did I take someone out of excruciating pain in a timely manner? Great. Next. So please release the idea that you should be a perfect little know-it-all. Be content with the idea that you ever being perfect is about as tangible as you catching the tooth fairy mid job. It ain't happening. Get comfortable with the unknown because that's where you become your strongest. That discomfort with the unknown will force you to learn, but don't give it a free pass to intimidate you! If a physician or patient asks you something you don't have an answer to, stop scrambling for an answer that isn't there. Wanting to appear perfect will make you do that. Humbly admit your uncertainty and focus your energy on finding the answer. It's a huge blow to the ego to not know, I get it. But there is so much relief in accepting that you don't need to have all the answers right now, or ever. Trusting your learning process involves trusting that what you don't know is leading you down the path to knowing.

We're all mastering a set of skills we see and use every day, but no one is perfect. We're human. We feel emotions. We're allowed to feel those emotions. Our coworkers upset us. Even our patients upset us.

Don't strive for perfection. Strive for progress. Clap for yourself every time you make some progress on this difficult journey to becoming an expert in your field. Take some time to appreciate the strength it takes to even begin this journey.

Abandon the idea of perfection. Abort the plan. Work towards improving, and never become complacent. Allow yourself to evolve. Allow your expectations to evolve.

But the next time you are looking for your super nurse cape, breathe easy knowing it doesn't exist. Relax, take a deep breath, and take perfection off your to-do list for the year. And remember, You are human first. Nurse, second.

Check your ego

When you forget that fear is of low vibrational energy and related to the ego, but courage is vibrating on a higher frequency, gently affirm to yourself:

Fear is just a playground for my ego.

YOUR EGO WILL RUN wild feeding off your fear if you give it enough space to do so. Why is that?

We all learned about the ego in psychology. Your ego helped guide and shape your experiences. It taught you how to navigate your world before you had any experiences to guide you. It pulled your id into alignment and told your superego to chill out a bit. The ego serves as the balancing part of our psyche. In a way, it is your friend. But in the spiritual sense, ego is not your friend. In this context, ego is not helping you, but is actually hindering your potential.

The ego develops within us when we forget to tap into our higher source; the infinite source. This could be God, Allah, the universe, or something else that is significant for you. When we disconnect from our source, we forget that we are spiritual beings having physical experiences and that there is no limitation to our abilities when we seek power and strength from that source. When you begin to rely and identify with just your physical body, you forget your infinite nature. You begin to focus on limitations rather than on the profound truth that you can indeed do anything you want if you seek that power to flow through you, like a plug attached to an outlet. Without that awareness, the ego becomes this overpowering, imbalanced voice in our minds. It sees opportunities to taunt you because you forget your self; your truest self. It disguises itself as a voice of reason when really, it's a voice of fear. It teaches you humility as a distraction from exercising your God-given talents. It forces you into a mask because it tells you that your authenticity won't be accepted. It intentionally blocks any part of you that resembles freedom from fear because the goal of the ego is to keep you small. It doesn't want you to learn your true power because it's competing with your truest self. If you're courageous enough to go for that specialty they told you wasn't possible for a new grad, well, the need for the ego dies. You won't rely on its advice anymore because you'll see the disconnect in what it is telling you versus what is actually possible.

Ego never wants to give you the opportunity to push past the fear to see what is possible for you as a new nurse. You must never know that becoming a travel nurse is easily achievable. Ego won't let that happen. Ego does not want you to know that it is all possible. Ego wants fear to resonate. In fact, ego uses fear to hold you back, to keep you small and safe. It wants you to fit back into your earlier years of what made you feel wanted. So you mimic those familiar behaviors to not rock the boat in any area of your life, including this new job. When you have a question, ego speaks up, "Don't ask that, you will look stupid." When you want to call the doctor, ego says, "If you call, they will think your findings are insignificant and scream at you." Ego is that little voice shouting all the horrible things at you that unsettle your spirit.

Until we reprogram and reset ourselves, ego will continually try to limit the infinite possibilities of self. Don't give ego a place to run wild in your mind. I could give you a cliché moment of encouragement and say that fear has no place in your heart when pursuing a goal. But that would be a blatant lie. Fear is all over the place running rampant when you go after a goal. Fear is what the ego uses to control you. Fear is what you wake up with and go to sleep with. When you give in to the fear, that's when you become anxious. That is when you become insecure about your abilities and become paralyzed. You stop wanting to try. That is when placing an IV feels impossible, so you never go for it and always call on someone else. When fear sets in, you stop advocating for your patients during rounds or when the doctor shows up because you feel your voice holds no weight. You stop having big goals and ambitions because ego uses fear to trick you into thinking none of it is possible. Fear makes your present unbearable and takes away your vision for more in your career.

You must choose to move with the fear. You must decide to have control over it. It's like a deep breath for your patient after abdominal surgery. You can choose to not take any deep breaths and then develop pneumonia, or you can choose to take smooth, deep breaths as you focus beyond the pain. That is how I need you to view fear. As a controllable emotion that you will choose to move through, breathe with, and find your peace in. Then you can focus on the goals ahead. And only then will the ego begin to lose its power and you begin to progress as a new nurse.

You see, half the battle is the unknown. You do not know it all, which leads to an intimidating space of uncertainty, and THAT leads to the fear. The ego has the most fun when you can't anticipate what comes next. This is the easiest time for it to play mind games with you. If I know what to expect in my day, my ego can't send a million messages of fear to me because I've already lived and experienced many similar days and I know what to expect. But when you're new, you have no idea what is ahead. You're just hoping for something that is familiar that you can manage. I remember as a travel nurse, right before every assignment started in the first two years, I'd get nervous. What kind of nurses would I work with? What kind of IV pumps do they use? What kind of ventilators do they have? Are the patients the same? Do they manage their patients the way I'm used to? I would be scared as hell, and my ego loved it. I was afraid to appear incompetent. I was afraid I wouldn't know how to do something the way they did and that they would judge me for it. But what about learning a new way? What about being confident expressing that I didn't know their way? What about surrendering to the unknown? What about releasing the need to control every moment? Those weren't options for me at that point. I know, I know. One second I am saying have control, and the next I am saying release it, but that my friends, is the beauty of life. Knowing when to submit and when to assert. It is a gentle balance that creates a sense of peace in our day.

By my fourth assignment in a new hospital, I realized that everybody does things a little differently. Instead of being deathly afraid of how not knowing their ways of doing things would make me look, I realized these were learning opportunities I was losing out on. My ego was tricking me into another false narrative about what I should know. I realized that these experiences would give me more courage to face my next assignments. I needed to embrace the unknown, no matter how they showed up. I needed to learn to stand in my truth and gain the experiences necessary to make me a stronger nurse.

Even the most experienced nurses cannot predict their day. Not one surgeon, no matter how many years or times they have operated, can tell you how their day will go with absolute accuracy. What they *can* tell you is that their experience allows them confidence in their approach. I may not know every diagnosis that walks in the door, but I do have the courage to say, "I can and will take whatever is assigned to me," within my scope of practice of course! I am not afraid of the unknown, but that comes only with experience. Those feelings of despair and chaos you get when assigned to a patient who has a diagnosis you have never heard of or do not remember will one day be replaced with poise. You will gracefully anticipate your days. You won't lose sleep over what's to come. You will not lose confidence in the opportunities that are meant for you to learn from. You will show up and embrace all that your day has to offer because you will trust that each of these moments add to the experiences that will make you a more wholesome and confident nurse.

Push through

When fear overwhelms you and you can't move,
gently affirm to yourself:

Courage does not come overnight.
It comes with experience.

FEAR CAN MAKE US want to stop. It paralyzes us, and we don't realize that where we have stopped is not a safe zone. But because what lies ahead is so uncertain, this dead zone feels comfortable. So, we wait. We hope that someone or something will save us. Sorry to break it to you, but ain't nobody coming! It's just you and those fears until one of you give in, and it must not be you. Only you can overcome this battle.

You need to find a guiding light to help you push through. Find your why! Remember that why and let it guide you. Maybe your why is the little girl or boy in you that dreamed of this moment of being a nurse. Maybe it's a parent or grandparent who inspired you to join this profession. Possibly a child you need to provide for. Maybe it's your financial situation that needs a stable career. I don't and will never judge your why, I just need you to remember it and use it as your weapon to destroy the fear that wants to eat you alive. You deserve to win this battle. Everything you overcame up until this point is begging you to ditch the fear and move through this moment! I know it can be emotionally draining. I know it will take every ounce of energy that you have. But you deserve more than to stop now. You deserve to push through. You deserve to prove to yourself that it is indeed possible. I trust that for you. Now you must take this baton I am handing you and trust yourself.

I have had to overcome so many doubts to get here. In my first semester of nursing school, my professor sent a letter home stating that I would fail nursing school if I didn't pull it together. Oh, I pulled it together. My preceptor at my first job as an adult med surge nurse told me that I was very robotic with my patients and I needed to show more interest. I remember she made me cry and didn't bat an eye at my pain. Zero empathy. Oh, but now I get awards for my patient care. Every corner you turn, someone or something is going to tempt you to stop, but you have to remember your goals, dreams, and aspirations above all. I remember going home alone to an empty apartment on my first travel assignment. What am I even doing in this lonely city? I thought. But here I am, thriving.

You have got to dig deeper. And when you feel like you gave it your all, take a rest and go even deeper. It's in you, I promise you it is, you just have to believe in this thing more than you fear it. Push through. The person you are on the other side of this mountain is counting on it!

Be like water

Because everything feels scary to you right now,
gently affirm to yourself:

I will embrace the rhythm of change.
I will begin to realize that every shift as a nurse
will be a completely
different dance I will eventually learn the moves to.

I USED TO BE so afraid of change. Every morning in the ICU, I would
have a mini heart attack when getting to know a new patient. Will
they desaturate? Will they code? How is this new family? How
will their set of doctors behave with me? I hated having to find
a new routine, learning new meds to give, having to conquer a
whole new flow to my day when I barely got through last week. I
would have preferred the same patient and diagnosis every shift
to pacify my discomfort.

But growth doesn't take place when you're comfortable. That
elevation in your skills and critical thinking abilities only come
through embracing every painful moment of learning something
new. The rhythm you must embrace as a nurse is not one of the
status quo, but one of constant flow. Be like water. Remain fluid.

Gracefully adapt to new environments. Get your skates on today, but have peace in knowing that tomorrow may require running shoes. And even when you get used to the instability of the skates and grow dependent on the support of the sneakers, nursing will throw a wrench at you and you may need to be barefoot.

It's all about changing. We are nurses. We are designed for this. We become our best selves when we get comfortable with giving all that is required of us in every moment, without allowing the fear of newness to distract us. Once, a short time after my orientation ended, I learned that my assignment had been changed from the comforts of my post-op CV patient I had been studying how to care for, to a neurosurgery patient. This is very normal, yet I still had a silent fit because of the change. For goodness sake charge nurse, I've been studying all the nursing implications for CV and today you want to give me Neuro. No ma'am, I don't want it. Take it back and give me what I had. The thing is, by day three, I had grown comfortable with the EVD and was ready to tackle the patient wanting to get up and out of bed. I was afraid on that first day because I just knew my patient was going to drain all the fluid out of their brain and herniate because I would forget to clamp it. I was afraid, but I did the work at home to reinforce how to manage my patient with an EVD. I returned to work more at ease, knowing what to expect. I knew the family, the patient's meds, and I had visualized in my head how this shift would be better than the day before. But then I got in, and the charge nurse had switched assignments around again! No, no, and no! I wasn't ready for another change! Just when I was ready for my EVD patient, boom, they hit me with a chest tube. My heart couldn't handle the situation that early on in my career. I wanted what I wanted because it made me feel safe. At that time I didn't understand the importance of continuity of care for my patients yet, but I relied on it for myself. If I knew what to expect from the patient I could better plan my day. If I knew what the doctor would ask because they asked it yesterday, I would feel like a stronger nurse. I wanted to feel like a good nurse, but at that point, every new patient made me feel stupid. New set of meds to review and understand. New plan of care to implement. All the newness on top of the newness was overwhelming. I didn't want to play with chest tubes on day three! I didn't watch all those EVD videos on YouTube for nothing!

I liked the security blanket of having the same patient day in and day out. I remember the first four hours of one shift with a new intubated patient was so intense for me that I could have easily had a heart attack. How would the patient react when I turned and repositioned them? Would they wake up? Would I need more sedation? Would they self-extubate? Those first few months were sickeningly stressful.

But for the sake of my growth, I needed to learn how to feel stable on shaky ground. I needed to learn how to be like water. I needed to have some faith in myself. I needed to trust that even when the beat changed, I would still be able to find my rhythm. It's like when you're out with your friends at a lounge vibing to some good music, you don't stop and get nervous when the DJ changes the song. No, you pivot to the next dance move. Most of the time you aren't even thinking about it; it comes naturally. That is the goal. To become adaptable. To be flexible. To bend it without breaking it and not have a panic attack in the process.

Imposter syndrome

When you doubt your abilities,
gently affirm to yourself:

*I managed to convince someone else I deserve this job.
I promise to spend the rest of my time convinc-
ing myself I am competent enough to keep it.
Even though some days I will not always believe
I am worth it, I promise to prove my doubts
wrong every shift I choose to show up.*

HAVE YOU EVER HEARD of something called imposter syndrome?
Imposter syndrome is a psychological game we unknowingly
participate in where we persistently doubt our accomplishments
and worthiness and we develop this unrealistic fear that someone will soon expose us as a fraud. Does that sound familiar? Do
you constantly doubt that you have the ability to be a competent
nurse? That even when you are competent, even when you do
things that make you proud, you still feel like it's too good to be
true and someone is going to find something you've messed up?
As if all those gruesome hours in school didn't prove to you that
you deserve every good thing that results from you surviving
that process.

I want you to know your worth and know that your worth isn't determined by the places your feet land. Your worth isn't fleeting. It doesn't change with circumstances. It doesn't change with the good and bad days. Your stock is always up! It withstands the changing climates. You need to believe that and feel that deep in your gut before others have the opportunity to dictate anything other than that truth to you. We need not convince others of our worth. Just walk in your light, and those around you will soon know it too.

Let me give you permission to be proud of yourself. Not that you need my permission, but let me remind you that you have permission to take pride in what you've accomplished. You survived one of the hardest undergraduate degrees to obtain while managing to keep your sanity. You then took one of the most notoriously intimidating licensing exams known on Earth. THEN you had the nerve to go apply for a job with absolutely no real experience in the field to which you were applying. And to add even more audacity to the situation, you actually convinced someone else that your lack of experience but really impressive degree qualified you to get that job, and they believed you! Looky here! You've accomplished a whole lot so far, and you deserve to remind yourself of that every time it gets hard. Too often we question what was divinely set aside for us. Whenever you feel challenged, remember that you fought for this moment. These challenging moments you are facing now are forcing you to grow. You might as well accept that nothing will feel easy from this moment on. You will have to fight for it, but eventually you will overcome your doubts and challenges. Remember that someone thought highly enough of you to bring you into these situations because they knew you would learn to overcome them. The joke is, that person was YOU! You believed in yourself before anyone else ever could. You trusted your knowledge enough to apply for a nursing position. You trusted your strengths enough to show up every day to learn, even though you knew that process would drain you physically, mentally, and emotionally. *You* did that! That alone should be the pep talk you give yourself on the days self-doubt shows up to have lunch with you. Kick that sucker out! Don't give self-doubt an invitation to your process. Cancel that pity party and continue to show up and show out; for you first, and then that same energy will radiate to your patients! You are deserving. Nothing was handed to you. And even that which was handed to you was deserved. You attract that which you believe you deserve. Start carrying yourself like you know that blessing is yours. Then know it for real.

During my first interview as a new grad nurse, I sweat so much down my back and under my legs that when I got up, the chair was soaked. I might as well have put a chucks pad down before I sat. I was so embarrassed, I didn't want to move away from the chair when the interview was over. I hovered over the seat with an awkward smile, hoping that it would dry as I said my goodbyes. Why was I so nervous? I had some very strong personalities asking me questions on how to handle situations I'd never even experienced, but I overcame that. I proved myself worthy to them, yet I didn't believe I was worthy myself. This was imposter syndrome in action.

In those early days of nursing, I had such a hard time seeing in myself what I was convincing others about me. My inner thoughts were contradicting my outer portrayal of who I was. When others asked how I was doing, I'd say fine, and maybe for that one second, I'd feel fine, but then my mind would take over and I would question my whole entire being.

I understand what it's like to feel like an imposter. I experienced those feelings as a new nurse and as a young woman trying to run her own business. Some mornings I would wake up and tell myself that I'm the bomb for having mentored all these new nurses and guiding them to realize their highest potential. Other mornings I woke up cringing at the thought that people actually thought I knew what I was doing. To overcome these feelings I had to work on consistently reminding myself that I did indeed know what I was doing, and practice owning that. I reminded myself of every nurse educator who wanted to sit down with me to learn my strategy. Every HR executive who scheduled meetings with me to learn my tricks. Every new nurse who came to me with their anxiety and left with confidence. I had to learn to toot my own horn. I had to remember the doctors who thanked me for my detailed and timely assessments. I had to remember all the good things on the days my mind would become overpowering. Because on the hardest days, I became my own worst enemy. I needed to remember how to become my own biggest cheerleader. I needed to remember how to silence the voice of the imposter that was causing me to second-guess myself. I needed to remember all the things I'd accomplished and remind myself of all the amazing things still ahead.

Get comfortable lifting your head high up to the sky because the world will give you enough reasons to want to look down. Take back control over your thoughts and remember, the you who once overcame will continue to overcome.

Affirmation

You belong everywhere your feet touch. You are sunshine. We need your presence. Your innocence brightens the room. Believe in your invincibility. You are received with arms open wide. Now I want you to repeat that. I want you to replace the "you" with "I" and make that your anthem.

"I belong everywhere my feet touch. I am sunshine. My presence is needed. My innocence brightens the room. I believe in my invincibility. I am received with arms open wide."

Activity: What brought you here?

We all need a little reminder every now and then to remember our greatness. I want you to practice this. Practice tooting that horn for yourself. For the hard days where you forget that you are worthy, write a list below of all the things you've accomplished so far. Revisit this list whenever you need to remember that you are overcoming.

_____

_____

_____

_____

_____

_____

_____

_____

_____

_____

_____

_____

_____

_____

_____

Slow down

On the days you are moving too fast,
gently affirm to yourself:

I will not rush.
I am taking my time.
Even when administration demands my speed,
I will remember that safety is a more important priority than
speed.

DON'T LET PEOPLE RUSH you. Let me say it again! But now imagine me adding my thickest Jamaican accent because I really need you to feel me. So again, don't let people rush you! Translation: Never allow anyone to force you into a pace that is faster than you're comfortable moving. Especially when it comes to care for our patients. You should always move at what is a healthy pace for you. Rushing causes mistakes. Pressure causes mistakes. And when those mistakes occur, you will be the only one left with the consequences!

Administration will rush you. The doctors will rush you. Your patients will rush you. Still, only move at a pace that does not compromise the quality of care you are providing. Of course there are moments where we'll move fast, like in a code or rapid response, but we never move faster than the pace that is safe. Always remember that. If moving faster compromises your ability to move and act safely, then you are no longer efficient and the risks outweigh the benefits, so you need to slow down.

Sometimes we need to pause and not get caught up in the work chatter; that background noise that makes you feel like you need to be doing more and more at the detriment of your patient's safety. It's never worth it to push against your own safety alarms. As nurses, especially new nurses, we constantly feel like we are racing against the clock. With labs due, meds due, and all the other things in between, it's so important that we learn to prioritize. Prioritizing helps us slow down. You don't have to run to give Colace, but you might need to run to draw blood cultures. But running to do one thing doesn't mean skipping all the safety stops along the way.

You need to find your pace. The pace that feels safe for your abilities in the beginning. Then own that pace.

I recall once, in the beginning of my career, I had to draw labs off an arterial line for a patient whose family was also anxious about me calling the physician. I knew I needed to have these labs drawn first or the call would essentially be pointless. Drawing labs off an arterial line for me at this point was very methodical. I needed to think through every step to not screw things up. I knew that, the family did not. They were just fixated on what they wanted me to do. So they stood over me as I drew my labs. Feeling all the heat on my neck and back, I still worked as methodically, slowly, and efficiently as drawing from an arterial line would allow. All while having the family complain to each other passive aggressively that they didn't want the physician to leave before I had a chance to call. So while I allowed them to carry on, I wasn't pressuring myself into speed to appease them and fail my patient. No,

I couldn't answer the family's questions right in that moment. No, I wasn't going to rush that very important step before calling the physician who is going to want these labs in anyway. No I wasn't going to allow anyone else to dictate my pace and compromise my quality. I commanded my pace because I realized that allowing others to pressure me into a pace that I wasn't comfortable with would cause me to mess things up. I would forget to draw one of the many labs ordered. I would forget to draw up a waste first and would subsequently ruin the lab values altogether.

Rushing never saved me time; it wasted my time because I would always end up having to repeat something I forgot. I had to get honest with myself about what I needed in order to operate safely, and I had to get more assertive with the people around me who demanded more than I could give. You can practice completing a task more efficiently, but never make speed the goal. That should never be the target. Completing a task faster should be the byproduct of moving more efficiently. Remember that! The goal is always to be safe and efficient, never to race against the clock. When you practice moving more efficiently and growing more comfortable with the flow of your day, you'll realize that it's the only way to slow down the clock in your favor.

Command the pace of the room and assert your right to a safe environment for you and your patients.

You are not alone

When you are feeling lonely on this long walk,
gently affirm to yourself:

Practicing as a new graduate nurse
is scary for everyone. We all feel things.
Just different things
at different times
expressed in different ways.
I will not make the mistake to believe I am alone in this.

HOW INTERESTING WE ARE as humans. To believe no one but us would be having a hard time. We create these isolating experiences and then trick ourselves into believing that we are all alone in it. The truth is, everyone is having their own unique experiences simultaneously. How you express your stress and frustrations may not be the way others express them. Nonetheless, we all still have our frustrations.

I used to work with a group of new grads who I thought had it all together. I mean everything, from their report sheets to their scrubs. I felt alone and sad and secretly resented the way nursing came so easy to them. Until I went out for drinks with some of them and we poured our souls out about the difficulties we were experiencing. I instantly heard my Jamaican mother in my head, "Don't watch people." In other words, stop comparing your experiences to another person's when you have no idea of their struggles. We all felt the same things, but no one felt vulnerable enough to admit it outside of the safety of our inebriation at that bar. It was liberating, and it felt good to relate.

Maybe you find your tribe at work with other new nurses who can be a shoulder to vent on, or maybe you don't find a soul to relate to. So you put on a game face every day because you don't trust your coworkers. Either way, know that you aren't alone in this process. Maybe the person who gets and understands you isn't on your unit, but trust me, we exist. Once upon a time we all fought through this phase. Be gentle with yourself. Give yourself some grace. Trust me, you aren't so unique that you would be the only nurse in a profession of 3.1 million to feel the feelings you feel right now. This is only a step on the ladder we take as we journey towards becoming experts. We all share this moment. It connects us. It's like an invisible string that keeps us all connected no matter where we take our careers. Every nurse started in this very vulnerable place of knowing nothing more than what we studied in our textbooks. You're never alone in this. Every nurse was once a novice. And the nurses who change specialties become novices all over again. The newly graduated NP is a novice. The educator who just graduated with their Master's is a novice. You see, at some point on this journey, we all must embrace the novice inside of us, trusting that we are never alone. Understanding that these challenges we learn to overcome are rites of passage. We all, at some point, had to learn how to strategize and use these struggles as a way to get closer to our wins. This book is your reminder that, at the very least, one other person knows what you are going through. That person is me.

Send fear away

When the failures of your previous day seem to haunt you for the
rest of the week,
gently affirm to yourself:

I am a great nurse. I am a great nurse.
I am a great nurse.
Even if my fear may sometimes whisper otherwise.

FEAR. OUR LITTLE UNINVITED guest. It shows up, pours itself a glass of
wine, and pulls up a chair right in our minds. The worst part is,
we know we didn't invite it in, we surely hate its company, but we
bring it snacks and a blanket to make it more comfortable anyway.
Why do we welcome the uninvited, unwelcomed guest to stay?

We have got to do better. Yes, I know. There is something about
starting a new thing that can leave you raw and vulnerable. Vulnerable to the negativities that are designed to make you shy away
from your greatness. This vulnerability makes us more susceptible
to the fear that comes with this new territory. But it's one thing
when fear sneaks in and an entirely different thing when you give
it permission to stay.

You know when you were young and your mother told you
not to do something and you did it anyway? And if you had my

luck, you'd have broken the rule she set and still had to call her to help you out as a result because you had no other way out of it. Mom: "Jannel, don't go to the city after school, go straight home." Jannel: "Ok Mom." Also Jannel: Ignores everything she just agreed to and gets on train, goes into the city after school and gets stuck downtown because the trains stop running early and she'd have to call Mom to come pick her up.

You know that dreadful feeling of fear that floods your body, like Oh em gee this can't be real? Yeah. That's the feeling I used to get anytime I had to call or page a doctor. Why God, why me? Couldn't I have just gone these 12 hours without ever having to give one update or say a thing? I hated communicating with the doctors.

But what exactly are we afraid of? Sometimes we have to push the fantasy and illusions we create in our minds out and replace it with some reality. Am I afraid of making a mistake? That's reasonable. But then ask yourself, what is my fear of mistakes actually doing to benefit me? Really ask yourself this. The fear itself is doing nothing. It is creating a sympathetic nervous system response, and then what? You're anxious. You feel paralyzed when it's time to get things done. You don't sleep before work. You dread your patient assignment. And then what? Nothing. Whew chile, that exhausted me just writing it out. We waste so much energy fearing and never doing. Never doing the things that are the antidotes to fear. Like getting a resource book and studying and not just showing up to work like the information is just going to jump into our brains. What about showing up on your shift earlier to review your patient assignment in advance? What about looking up the side effects of the medication before you administer? What about asking the other nurses on your unit for their professional opinion on what to do next?

You see what I did there? I gave you so many other things to do before the fear sets in and once the fear sets in. Real life, actionable steps.

The better you get at knowing your patient and their needs, the easier it is to give a suggestion on their behalf. In my English class in the ninth grade, I used to hate it when Mr. Nardone would ask me what I felt about a very significant moment in the novel we were reading. You know why I hated it? Because I never read it, at least not thoroughly enough to form an opinion of my own. Who wants to speak about something they know nothing about? Yes, let me offer you this critique of the literature I read while watching my favorite shows and chatting to my BFF all night.

The courage to do the necessary will come when we are willing to do the work.

Don't allow the fear to take over your body. Stop it at the door. Hi, thank you for your concern fear, but we're good today. That's it. Don't make your fearful thoughts become a habit that whisks you off into wonderland making up all kinds of falsehoods. Because if your imagination is anything like mine, you'll have bubble guts in no time with all the stories you can make up about what comes next.

Next time fear starts swindling its way in, look it dead in the face and proclaim loud and clear, "I am indeed a badass nurse and we don't need your help in discerning that!"

Have some courage for the day ahead

When you need to give yourself permission to have courage for the difficult days ahead,
gently affirm to yourself:

Yesterday I worked with fear.
Today I will step past it.

THERE IS SO MUCH power in acknowledging that this whole thing is really freaking scary. A release happens when we admit out loud that we are scared beyond what we let on. We are scared, and that is normal. Everything we do matters. If I pull up one milliliter more than I should for my pediatric patient, I could overdose them and will have to deal with some serious consequences. That's intimidating. If you choose to ignore your patient's headache complaints because you don't know what to do about it, you could be running off to CT later in the evening to find out you should have notified the doc sooner. That's a lot to swallow.

Growing up, my aunt used to say to us, "when you walk into this house, leave those nasty habits you picked up outside at the door. When you leave back out, do as you please with them, just don't walk them in here." While my adult self has 10 million rebuttals for that, I also understand what she was saying. Don't bring your bad habits home because they won't be tolerated here.

Why not have the same attitude with our fears? Leave those bad boys at the door. Don't bring them to the bedside with you. Let your fears know, "I know you've been following me everywhere I go, but my patients really need me in here and I just can't have you clouding my judgment." Make a swap. Choose to leave your fears right at the door, and as you enter that new territory, welcome your confidence to go with you instead.

Some of our days are so difficult that the thought of getting up another day to do it all over again is daunting. The thought of the unknown that is yet to come is a challenge to process. The thought of managing that same very sick patient again tomorrow is mentally exhausting.

I once had a patient with a very difficult wound-care regimen. It probably wouldn't be difficult to my experienced nursing self now, but boy, was it difficult for my new nursing self. I had to perform wound care twice on my shift, and I hated it because I couldn't get it as perfect as the nurse before me. Every minute that came closer to the hour I had to perform wound care would make me more nauseous from my anxiety because I knew the patient and their family would analyze and criticize my technique to death. I wondered why they didn't just ask to not have me back. It would have made all our lives easier. Those three shifts and six attempts at that wound care were gruesome, but every time, I committed to releasing the fear and getting better. I promised myself that even though I was scared, I would let some of that fear go every time I attempted the wound care, and I would pay closer attention to the steps that felt hard for me. I promised to ignore and not take the family's attitude and comments personally because as I learned in nursing school 101, this was just their form of controlling the uncontrollable. No matter how many more times I would need to perform that wound care, I committed to being less fearful the next time.

That's the secret to surviving your first year as a new nurse. It's to find one little thing you'll commit to mastering every day, until you eventually check all the little things off your list. It's a journey we're taking. Break the journey up into bite-sized, digestible pieces, and the fear will be broken up with it. If I commit to mastering a few small changes tomorrow, the whole day ahead doesn't feel so scary. I know the little things I have promised myself to work on, so the fear attached to the whole process isn't flooding my brain all at once. The only fear I need to deal with is the fear of the few little things I've prioritized and committed myself to for the week. Then, little by little, there will be fewer things ahead to be fearful of. The unknown of the journey is sickening, but vow to learn something new every day that will help you start unpacking the fear.

I know confidence can feel really tricky for most of us. You think, "I'm too new to be confident." But, no, you aren't. Confidence is not arrogance. It isn't a know-it-all attitude. Confidence is a gentle feeling that shows others you can be trusted with whatever it is you came to do. That means knowing what you are great at and displaying those strengths but understanding your limitations and getting help when needed. These are all are signs of confidence that don't require 10 years on the job for others, including yourself, to recognize.

Ask yourself, "Would I be content walking away before I even tried to overcome the nerves? Would I be curious about the what ifs of my potential? Would I be ok with that untapped potential just left untouched, or would I want to see myself do more? Wouldn't you want to know you tried harder? As hard as you could?

Well, that's courage. That is exactly what it means to use the power of your courage to move forward. It's going beyond all that your fear is telling you and daring to see what lies on the other side of all that. It's acknowledging that you're scared as hell and trusting the possibility of growth.

Don't tolerate the fears. Don't tolerate them infringing on your personal space. They will not respect your boundaries. They will crowd your space and tell you what they want. They will make a permanent home in your practice. Before you know it, fear will be guiding every decision you make. Put the fear down. Shake it off your back. Drop that bad boy at the door. Kick that thang off your doorstep. Whatever you do, don't welcome it to the workplace with you.

It takes so much courage and, of course, a bit of insanity to keep returning to the greatest challenges of our lives every day in the hope of finding the joy in mastering it. But that's what nursing is. An insanely fulfilling profession. One can't witness others straddle the fence of life and death every day without first facing their own fears and overcoming them.

Affirmation

Repeat after me:

I am limitless.
My power is infinite.
I radiate.
I am magnetic.
Everything I need, I attract.
I am my most competent self at all times.
I am the nurse my unit has been waiting for.

Amen.

Eliminate doubt

Because some things need to be released,
gently affirm to yourself:

I will not give myself the benefit of the doubt;
I will eliminate the doubt altogether.

I THOUGHT I WOULDN'T curse in this book. Then I realized it's my book and I have the right to express myself in any way I see fit. So, my next piece of advice will be to go ahead and eliminate that shit! Let go of the self-doubt that is eating you alive. It ain't doing much for you! It follows you everywhere you go. If you go left, it's there telling you to go right; if you go right, it's telling you how dumb you are for not staying in the same spot. Self-doubt is not working for you any which way you decide, so let it go. The more you feed into it, the more it has to say about everything you do.

Self-doubt isn't your best friend giving you some tough love to help you improve. It's the hater talking about you behind your back. The hater you can't please, no matter what you do. You wouldn't let that "friend" hang around, so why encourage your self-doubt to? Let it go! Why not give yourself the benefit of the doubt? Why question your abilities so much that you're willing to have that doubt linger in your mind?

You worked too hard to have doubt make your voice crack when updating the physician. You deserve better than wondering if you saw or heard what you assessed because you don't trust yourself. Allowing doubt in becomes a habit. The more we second-guess ourselves, the more it becomes a habit to believe our judgment is wrong.

This is your foundation year. It will set the tone for your whole career. If every day you think you're wrong, then when will you begin to trust that you might be right?

Today, I want you to release your doubt. Instead of allowing the doubt to trap you, start finding more concrete evidence to push the doubt out and build your confidence in who you are as a nurse. What did you hear when you listened to your patient's lungs? What is happening with your patient that might support that? What are the consequences of this matter if left untreated because you doubted yourself? Give yourself some logic to separate the thoughts your doubt has created. It's easy to convince yourself that you're wrong with doubt lingering around, but do you know how hard it is to convince yourself that you're wrong when you lay out the evidence to prove you're right? What we're not going to do is allow that doubt to be our guiding light on this journey. Nope. We have to work past it so that one day you'll begin to realize that believing in yourself is more important than the doubt you may be feeling.

Stop underestimating your skill, straighten your back, lift your head up, and learn to add some weight to the magnificence you're carrying. Nothing is light about what you can do. It's weighty. It's important! Start acting like it. Everything about your journey was arranged perfectly for you, so start acting like you deserve to be here. Stop underestimating all that you were made to do and start overestimating your confidence. Of course, don't overestimate your confidence so much that you do harm. But what I do want you to receive from this is that you are more confident than you realize.

We play ourselves down because of fear. The fact that I don't finesse that lab draw as perfectly as the nurse who has been here for 10 years must mean that I am not good at lab draws at all. Insert eye roll here. Give yourself more credit and try! When I first started placing IVs, blood would be everywhere. Not cute or neat! The families would look at me like their kid needed a blood transfusion after I was done. They probably did! The point is, I never stopped trying just because I was afraid of how it looked. I did not downplay my skill of getting the IV in just because it wasn't as pretty as someone else's placement.

Can you recall a moment this week where your fear of not knowing how to execute a task got the best of you? How did you manage to move forward? Or did you work with the anxiety until it subsided? Maybe the anxiety that comes with the self-doubt absorbed you so much that you eventually screwed up the thing you were working hard at?

There will be moments that cause you to feel uncertain. This is a normal part of the nursing journey. Uncertainty should make you do a self-check. Take a pause. Pauses are needed in all areas of life. The key is to not allow doubt to make you underestimate your skills. If you practiced it, did the research behind it, and received guidance on how to execute it, then trust that you can do it. Your nerves and doubt are your built-in alarm system. They say "Hold up! Are you sure we got this? Or do we need help?" They aren't saying, "You don't know what you are doing. Don't try because you'll screw this up."

Retrain your mind. Nerves are simply yield signs. Look around and make sure you are clear before proceeding. Nerves are not dead ends that prompt you to turn around and not keep going.

Remember that the next time you underestimate your ability to execute one of your nursing skills. Be confident and remind yourself you did the work. With every step we take forward, we leave doubt, fear, and negative self-talk behind!

You have the tools

When the lesson of trust repeats itself many times until you get it, gently affirm to yourself:

*I trust that I know all that is needed
to safely get through each moment.*

EVERY NOW AND THEN you need to remind yourself that you've got this. You have the tools needed for everything you will face. You have been equipped with the magic to maneuver the moment. This isn't a conversation about if you have it, this is about rebuilding the trust with yourself to believe it. I had to accept the fact that knowing how to get through the moment safely was not always about knowing the diagnosis or treatment plan by heart. My magic was trusting that I knew the basics. My magic was starting with a set of vitals and my assessment. Knowing my limitations. My magic as a new nurse was knowing when to ask for help. Knowing where to look to find the answers. My magic was in my identifying my resources and using them. My magic was acknowledging that I do not know it all, and that was my first safety net. Realizing I don't have all the answers was how I got through each moment safely. This allowed me to page the doctors sooner, call my charge nurse over, call the pharmacy with my quick questions. Trusting my abilities every moment thereafter was the key.

Trust that you'll know when to seek help. Trust that your ego isn't so fragile that you would compromise your patient's safety to avoid feeling stupid. Safely getting through a moment is sometimes as simple as asking for help. We're a team. You don't ever have to go through any moment alone.

Another reason you haven't learned to trust that you have all that it takes is because you haven't addressed your limiting beliefs around your abilities. You haven't addressed the negative self-talk. If you don't believe you're a strong nurse, that thought process will spill over into everything you do, and that can become dangerous. You'll overthink all the moments. You won't believe the first set of thoughts that come to your mind. You'll begin to devalue your own critical thinking. You have all the tools you'll need to get through each and every moment as they come. If you don't believe me, write it out and convince yourself. You have legs that can run to get help. A voice that can scream for backup. Arms that can check pulses and perfusion. A brain that can instinctively go into autopilot to begin stabilizing your patient. You always have the tools you need on hand to get through the difficult moments, you just need to trust yourself.

Listen and grow

When your stethoscope feels more like decoration for your scrubs than an actual tool to save lives,
gently affirm to yourself:

*Although I don't always know or recognize
what I am hearing, I vow to grow in sync with
the sounds my stethoscope reveals to me.*

I REMEMBER A TIME when my stethoscope felt pointless. I could not distinguish the sounds emitting from it. Crackles sounded like rales, but then I found out rales were crackles. At one point I wasn't even confident with the basics of clear breath sounds because I knew there had to be a trick, and clear just wasn't clear. I grew more frustrated every time I used the stethoscope. This became a stressor in my nursing life because it was obvious that as a nurse, I needed this thing in almost every moment. I initially chalked it up to the brand. Three stethoscopes in, I realized it was me. To my disappointment, the blame game was over and I needed to accept my accountability for my ignorance in the matter.

Here is what I need you to understand. Every one of us started at a point where the stethoscope was merely decorative. It's tricky! Our patients vary in size and diagnoses. No two patients are identical! And quite frankly, there is so much information being thrown at you right now, so many sounds to distinguish between, from breath sounds to bowel sounds, it's very easy to become overwhelmed, even with the simple stuff. But if sounds are an issue for you, then practice listening to everyone and everything! All while being gentle with yourself.

This also applies to every challenging area of nursing for you. Maybe it's not the stethoscope giving you the blues; maybe it's another important piece of equipment on your unit. Practice touching and using it. The goal is to get to the point of mastery. You must become the master of the things you feel the most challenged by. Nursing is sometimes a by-any-means necessary task. I used to listen to my dog's heart and breath sounds with my stethoscope! As a new grad in orientation, I went from room to room listening to every patient on my unit. This patient has crackles? Great! May I listen? We have expiratory wheezes here? I'll be right in! Diminished breath sounds at our lower bases? Got it! I'll take a listen! In order to overcome my fear, I had to be willing to look my obstacle dead in the face. Sometimes we fear the things we aren't good at because it reminds us of our weakness, and nobody wants to be around the thing they suck it. So we avoid it. But I became better at knowing what I auscultated by placing it on my priority list of things to do. Ignoring it wasn't going to change my weakness around it. In fact, ignoring your problems seems to accelerate the time it takes to come back and bite you in the butt. If I ignored my problems with breath sounds, then I would have eventually delayed care for patients with abnormal breath sounds requiring intervention.

Make a vow today to work at the things that feel the hardest for you right now. Set a goal for the week for how many times you'll expose yourself to that thing and stick to it. The only way to ensure your progression is through practice. I never used to feel empowered to use my stethoscope. I was basically afraid of it because I felt like it was betraying me. All the things I had gone through to get to that moment, yet sounds from a stethoscope were tripping me up? I mean, you expect harder things to disrupt your flow, not the most obvious thing you need to do. You can imagine how often I needed to use the damn thing in the pediatric ICU. But that's the point. Anything that challenges you is forcing you to rise to the occasion. It reveals your weakness to you then shows up every day until you master it. That's how this thing goes.

Back in nursing school, I once looked my community clinical instructor in the face and told her I couldn't hear my patient's heart sounds. She looked at me. I looked back at her. "I don't hear a thing miss." In my weak defense, my patient was obese, and the adipose tissue coupled with my awkwardness around patients meant I couldn't hear a heartbeat. It's laughable to think back to that audacity now; that I allowed a little fat to defeat me, but I never missed another heart sound after that. I was so embarrassed that I genuinely heard nothing. After enough of those experiences, I made it my mission to hear every beat, missed beat, rub, murmur, crackle, and rhonchi I could. I eventually became the nurse who was responsible for identifying abnormal sounds independently.

That's the attitude to adopt. A weakness is revealed and boom! You're on a mission to improve it; to master it. Today, it's decoration. Tomorrow it's how we diagnose. It's how we intervene. The stethoscope won't just be this cute graduation gift from family, it'll be an empowerment tool we use to advocate and carry out the necessary interventions for our patients.

Activity: Create a gratitude list

When I find myself having a very stressful day, I notice one key behavior I almost robotically engage in: I complain. I don't mean just a venting session and I'm done, I mean I complain the situation to death. Then before you know it, everything around me is agitating. Now the sun is too bright, or the music is too loud, or the patient is annoying. Now work is annoying and now I'm so far down the complaint hole that I'm actually considering quitting. Do you see that trend? Something frustrates me, it elicits a stress response, and I don't manage the stress in a healthy way. I choose the path of least resistance and go with the annoyance that has built up.

But this phenomenon can also work in a brighter and more positive way. Imagine if I start every morning with gratitude! Imagine if, for the first two minutes of me opening my eyes, I go through a list of things I am grateful for and excited about. Imagine that when something stressful occurs, I am able to express one small piece of gratitude about that moment. Imagine if instead of going down the complaint hole, I ascend up the gratitude latter. Imagine I have the power to lift my vibration. Well, no need to imagine, because we all possess that sort of magic. But for some of us, the path of 'positivity first' has not been traveled often. So when faced with a difficult situation, our brains opt for the path that has been tried and tested, clear of all debris and requires no work to get through. If we always resort to anger first, our brain wants that route first. The more we become intentional about choosing the path of positivity, the more our brain begins to plow through it. The leaves get swept away and the road becomes clearer. Our brain quickly realizes, I like this new path. Our heart rate doesn't spike, our muscles don't tense up; we don't have to send so many signals for the nerves to fire off in 10 different directions. Our brain starts naturally taking us down the path of positivity. It takes intentional behavior to create a different response.

Start with the simple activity of expressing gratitude daily. When you speak positively and share your gratitude, whether in writing or speaking them out loud, you raise your vibration. When you elevate your vibration, you begin to move in a completely different realm. This realm allows you to perceive and receive information back to your brain in a completely different way. A way that reflects the positivity that exists in life. You see, what we attract is a mirror of where our mental and emotional state is currently at. When we are miserable and tired, we seem to attract more of the misery around us. Everything is bothersome and stressful. But when we're positive and radiant, everything around us feels just as positive and radiant. Even the unexpected feels manageable and our mind begins to perceive these surprises as simple obstacles that we CAN overcome rather than major road-blocks that are impossible to move. Perception is so important in this journey we are on as new nurses. How we perceive our new career can singlehandedly affect our morale for what is ahead. When we perceive our time management as something that will forever be problematic, we no longer actively work towards the solutions. We sit in the defeat of it and allow it to take over our day. You'll make the mistake of waiting for time to 'fix' it and then remain resentful at how horrible your day always feels at the bedside.

Your perception and the way you speak to guide that perception is vital to your performance as a new nurse. If you are in a perpetual mode of gratitude, time management is not some impossible mysterious skill you must conquer. Your gratitude reminds you that having this job is a gift that not all new grad nurses are afforded. It reminds you that you are so special for being granted this opportunity to work with your patient population. It reminds you how lucky you are to have the chance to work at improving your time management skills daily rather than sitting home hoping for a callback. You see the difference in that? Change your words, and you change your life!

This is why a spirit of gratitude is so important. The more gratitude you continually practice expressing, the more things you attract to yourself to be grateful for. Negative emotions can't co-exist in a space of gratitude. Negative emotions can't hang around for too long when you are shouting at the mountaintop about all the things you are grateful for.

Start where you are, big or small. I like to start with the things that are particularly challenging for me. The things that stir my spirit, and not in a good way, are the things I try to find the positive in to express gratitude for. That annoying charge nurse who always gives you an admission?

"I am so incredibly grateful for this charge nurse who gives me the opportunity to master the flow of an admission into my day."

"I am so incredibly grateful that I was able to pass my NCLEX."

"I am so incredibly grateful for this new profession I have earned my right to be a part of."

"I am so incredibly grateful for the opportunity to be a part of a team that contributes to the healing of those who are sick."

How can one possibly stay in negativity when speaking so positively about their own life? Start expressing gratitude for all the things you have and even the things you want to have and accomplish in your career. Express it as though you already have them. Speak things into existence. Always remember that your thoughts can and will become reality. What you think inspires how you behave, which in return will result in that very thing manifesting itself if you believe it and work at it hard enough. That means the good and the bad!

I want you to write out everything you are grateful for below. Small or big. Change your words! Lift your vibration! Go!

_____

_____

_____

_____

_____

_____

_____

_____

_____

_____

_____

_____

_____

_____

_____

_____

_____

_____

Remember your passion

When the passion is dying and you need your purpose to lead the way,
gently affirm to yourself:

*I will remember the excitement and passion I felt
for my career on the day I passed my boards, but I
promise to dig deeper to find my purpose to get me
though the days I question this career choice.*

IT'S SO EASY TO forget the passion you once felt for a thing when that thing has become a source of stress. A month or two ago you were poppin' bottles, taking shots, finding a reason to celebrate every little thing because you finally became a nurse. Now it doesn't feel so easy to feel inspired. Now, the alarm clock in the morning has become an annoying little reminder of the day ahead instead of an exciting reminder of your privilege. Now you aren't hopping and skipping for that call bell that has already been rung four times in one hour by the same patient. It feels different. Stress always changes the lens through which we view life. What was once the best thing that ever happened to you is now looking a bit different. It's foggy. It's skewed. The lens needs a bit of cleaning, or rather, a bit of gratitude to help you remember that this still is the best thing that has ever happened to you. It's just challenging right now.

I get it. I've been there. As you grow through this process, that first taste of excitement you felt on day one will no longer sustain you. You will need to dig deeper. You need to start transitioning from passion into purpose. Ask yourself: What is my motivation for continuing this difficult process? Who am I impacting? What do I want to change? It's real cute in the beginning when you're shopping for new scrubs and a lunch bag, but it's not so cute when you haven't gotten a break and you've been running for the past seven hours. Passion ignites the flame; purpose maintains it. Passion is the emotion that excites you to start. Purpose is the strength to push forward when the emotion has faded. Because it will. Emotions are fleeting. Some days you're happy, other days you're defeated. If your commitment to nursing is merely led by passion, you won't give it your all on a bad day. You might just hand in your resignation letter. Purpose operates whether it's a good day or a bad day. Purpose leads you beyond the physical nature of the situation, and your mental strength begins to kick in. You move differently when you are motivated by your purpose.

So find your purpose in this and remember it always. When I became a pediatric ICU nurse, my passion was working with children. They are fun and vibrant and resilient even in the grimmest situations. I found my purpose in that in the beginning. My purpose was to be an advocate for the healing of very sick children within my community of the Bronx. I looked like my patients and their families, I spoke like them, I was relatable. I did not take that lightly. But I always had a desire to teach. So I co-founded Novice is the New Nurse. My passion for teaching led me to mentoring new nurses. But that wasn't easy to continue. My new purpose, mentoring new nurses and making sure they don't feel isolated and anxious through this process, is what kept me going when I wanted to give up. Even when my emotions weren't in it, I still mentored my nurses. Even on the days I wasn't into it, my purpose was bigger than just a desire to do something that seemed cool. My passion aligned with my purpose, and therefore the goal was sustainable.

So find your purpose in this. Dig deeper than just the reason you started. Find the reason that's supporting you through the hard days. But that doesn't mean forgetting the excitement. Keep the excitement you had in the beginning and find more moments of excitement as you journey. Patient gave you a compliment for the first time? A more experienced nurse acknowledged your progression? You finally gave your meds on time and found room to sit down? All those small wins matter. Those pieces of excitement will reignite the passion for your purpose. So dig deeper. And when you feel like you've gone deep enough, lean further into that constantly evolving purpose.

Activity: Remember your why

Why did you become a nurse?

Be your most honest self. Do not sugarcoat this answer. No one will see this. This may be your secret to keep deep within, or you may choose to shout it to the mountain tops. But in order for you to maneuver this profession, your answer is imperative. It teaches you self-reflection. It will help you remain disciplined. Whether you are here for money or born with this passion, be honest. Don't lie to yourself.

Because in order for you to keep going on the days things get difficult, you have to know your why. It will keep you inspired. It will keep you on track. It will keep you grounded and it will also help you understand when it is time to move forward. Your why will help you pivot when your actions no longer align with it. Your why is your mission. Know your why. Keep it close to your heart.

When your coworkers piss you off, remember your why. When your patients feel too challenging, remind yourself of your why. Allow your why to evolve with you. As you grow, revisit and revamp that why. But always be aware of it. And make sure that everything you do honors it.

Write down your why in the space below.

_____

_____

_____

_____

Do I fit?

When you are unsure whether or not this is a good fit for you, gently affirm to yourself:

Today feels like I do not fit any specialty.
I will be gentle with my indecisive nature.
My calling will reveal itself in the right time and on time.

SO MAYBE YOU HAVEN'T found your passion in nursing yet. Maybe you aren't sure what your purpose is yet. Maybe you're still deciding if you like where you currently are. It's ok to not have a home in nursing as yet. Sometimes we take the first thing that comes our way. In medicine, we know what it is when we know what it's not. It's how we come to a definitive diagnosis. We rule some things out. It's the same thing when trying to find your place in this nursing thing. The place that feeds your soul and fuels your excitement. The place you feel that passion. When I first started on an adult oncology unit, I didn't feel like it was speaking to my heart. Because I was new, I only got the med-surg patients. Had I maybe got to learn some oncology, I may have felt a little more excited about it all. I had fantasized about my first job, how nice my preceptor would be, and how much money I'd make doing what I absolutely love. I expected magical butterflies roaming around my tummy before each shift. I wanted so badly to love it, but I didn't. I hated my first nursing job. I wasn't connected to it. The people were not my tribe. I'm not sure if the frustrations of my new grad journey turned me off or if I just wasn't meant to be that kind of nurse. With all that uncertainty I was experiencing, I also felt guilt for having the audacity to desire something else when some of my peers were struggling to find jobs.

I always knew pediatrics was where I really wanted to be, but I allowed the opinions of others to stifle that dream in exchange for the 'foundation of med-surg.' But med-surg didn't move me. I wasn't passionate about it. Many people enjoy med-surg. They are passionate about it, but that just wasn't me. I now know that it was totally normal for me to desire more, or rather, more of what I wanted and less of what others thought I needed. I didn't fit the specialty because it was not what I desired for myself. Where you believe you feel a true fit is where you'll be the most beneficial. No one goes above and beyond for something they hate! You give the bare minimum.

This is why it's so important that you remain tuned into your behaviors. Are you drawn to your specialty? Are you really curious about the details of your patient population, or are you just showing up because you have to? This makes a difference in how you see your patients and care for them. It was great for me to question whether I enjoyed what I did. It's even more acceptable for you to not know where you go next or where you feel the most alive. This is all new for you. You are still learning to understand yourself as a nurse, as a person, and now you think you should know your forever specialty? Not possible. Take the pressure off yourself and allow your spirit to guide you. Nursing is so vast. As you get to know more about what you like and don't like as a nurse, things will begin to reveal themselves. There are so many options and opportunities out there; stay informed about them.

It's also very important that you learn to be able to discern between not liking a specialty and not liking the learning curve that comes with the specialty. Everything is challenging when you don't have the knowledge base and the tools to maneuver a situation. Just know that running from one unit to the next because you feel challenged will never solve your issue of belonging. Every specialty and unit will come with its fair share of difficulties. Not feeling like you belong because you are not passionate about a thing is very different from not feeling like you belong because the specialty itself is complex. You'll know when you've found your home.

Maybe you never find a home. Maybe every few years you challenge yourself in a new area. That is your prerogative. Don't let anyone dictate how this should look for you. It's your profession. Your decision. Ask management if it's possible to shadow on another unit. Figure out what you like about your current specialty and see if any other specialties give you more of that. Take your time with this. Nursing is a marathon, not a sprint. You'll find what resonates perfectly with your spirit, but you have to remain open to the idea that there is more for you if you want it.

You deserve this

On the days you wonder if you deserve to be here, gently affirm to yourself:

I deserve a seat at the table. I do not owe anyone any reasons why or any 'because.' I prove those answers every day that I show up and give my best even when I feel weighed down by the growing process of being a new nurse.

YOU DON'T NEED TO explain to anyone why you deserve to be here. Direct them to the State Board of Nursing website and have them search for your credentials if they need to know any further details. Those letters behind your name are the only whys or becauses anyone needs from you. You deserve your job. You deserve that pay. You have the right to speak up for your patients. You have the right to advocate for yourself. You went through school. You hold a degree. You passed your NCLEX. You now hold a license to practice in your state. You got through an interview. You passed your background check. I mean, do you need me to give you any more reminders why you deserve a seat at the table that is nursing? Didn't think so!

Nexxtttt.

Friends and allies

When you need permission to protect your heart as a new nurse, gently affirm to yourself:

> *I realize my sense of security as a nurse is fragile right now. I release those who attack my work and make me feel small because I am learning. Just like my personal friendships, I vow to only surround myself with those at work who foster my growth through encouragement, constructive criticism, and extra coffee when I need it.*

5/5/13

"—— is gonna break you, this hospital will break you...you watch!"

THAT WAS ONE OF my journal entries from 2013. (I won't mention which hospital or which nurse *Side Eye*.) A nurse who I looked up to uttered these words to me. I was vulnerable. Impressionable. Yet she offered these words to me as some sort of twisted advice. I rejected her words immediately. I told myself I would not take on that sort of negative energy in my life. Being a new nurse was hard enough; I did not need further discouragement as I journeyed through what felt like the impossible. I guess I had so many words from so many tired nurses already that I did not want another thing added to the list of "what's gonna happen to me."

As a new nurse, take care in nurturing your environment. That includes avoiding those who do not support your growth. Those who ruin your experience before you even get a chance to develop your own opinions. You do not need anyone to "fill you in" on what the issues, ahem, gossip of the hospital is. Eventually you will see and find out for yourself. Form your own opinions. In the meantime, all of that is clutter and distraction from your true focus, transitioning into this complex role. So just as you would in your personal life, save room for those who want to love on you, and get comfortable escorting to the door those who create clutter and chaos in your space. You don't need any more negativity. You've got enough all by yourself. When you allow others to sway your perception, you create more limiting belief patterns. The people you *should* be concerned about are the coworkers who are encouraging you. The patients who are waiting on you to show up in your fullness but don't make you feel like crap in the meantime.

Your coworkers come with their own set of baggage. You don't need to help them with their load. Allow their perception to be just that, and you allow your own to remain sacred. What needs to be revealed to you will find its way to you when necessary. That nurse who warned me about the hospital gave me bad advice, but I'm sure she meant well. Remember, the road to hell is paved with good intentions. Sure, she wanted to warn me of what she thought was ahead, but she forgot to account for her experiences that led to her distaste for the hospital. She was burnt-out. Tired. Wanting more out of life and projecting on to me. That wasn't fair. Had I absorbed her words, maybe I wouldn't have been so involved on my unit the way I was. They might have resonated so deeply because I admired her that I would have just done the bare minimum each shift and gone home. But that wasn't me. I was the girl who wanted to participate in making my unit better. I went out with my coworkers. I enjoyed chatting with administration even though everyone hated them. I quickly realized how important it was to hang with the positive nurses on my unit. The ones who still had hope. The ones who wanted to learn more. The nurses who weren't afraid to give more of themselves because they still had a lot left. The nurses who weren't burnt-out.

Your experiences as a new nurse are sacred. They shape you. That includes what and who you allow into your mind and your space. Work isn't any much different from your personal life. Your morals and values remain the same. You will still need your same boundaries. Go find your tribe. The ones who align with what you want to feel and see for yourself. The ones who encourage you to go for more on your unit because you want to, not the ones discouraging you because they are weighed down by their own stress and discomfort and not recognizing your potential. You become much like the people you spend the most time with, even at work. You have a choice in the company you keep at work. You don't have to engage in anything that is distressing or unsettling to your spirit. Guard your mind the way you do your nursing license. It is the foundation of your practice.

Growth in uncertainty

When you didn't know that you didn't know,
gently affirm to yourself:

> *I can't ask the questions I do not know exist. I am patient*
> *and I trust my experiences. I will allow questions to grad-*
> *ually reveal themselves to me as I advance my skills.*

YOU CAN'T EXPECT TO know all the questions you need to ask right
away. When you start a new journey in life, whether in your rela-
tionships, friendships, or career, you have to feel the space out
first before you get an idea of the things you have no clue about.
I know some of these reminders feel like a mouthful, but try to
understand.

Have you ever been in a situation where you didn't know that
you didn't know something? Like one of those situations where
your coworker says to you, "you should have asked me," and you
didn't even know there was something to ask. Being a new nurse
can be filled with lots of those moments. But let me reassure you,
there is no possible way to seek answers for questions you did
not know you had.

Let me give you a better example. When I started on my new
unit in the PICU, I had a patient who had not urinated in over nine

hours. When I told my preceptor about it, she asked me whether I checked my patient's bladder with the bladder scanner to see if there was any urine in there at all. She wanted to know if it was urinary retention versus straight dehydration. Insert emoji with the big surprised eyes here! I had no idea that was even a thing at the time. I didn't know that I should be asking myself or her those questions. I didn't know I should be asking for the bladder scanner at the eighth to ninth hour because I had no idea that we could estimate the amount of urine in a bladder via ultrasound and that it was a nursing intervention. You can't ask the questions you do not know exist. How would I have known prior to that experience that I should be inquiring about a bladder scanner before I called the physician? I took that experience for what it was and did not allow myself to feel defeated. My ignorance was to be expected. Some things nursing school just won't cover, but I embrace the fact that each situation I encountered as a newbie allowed me the opportunity to add another thing to my tool belt. I allowed the questions and answers to slowly but surely reveal themselves. Experience and doing shows you where you lack a particular understanding. Without going through the day-to-day stuff, you won't know what you don't know.

So be patient with yourself. Everything will become obvious within its time. Will some of that take intentional effort? Probably. But you can't ask for what you don't know exists. So expose yourself to more things that will lead you down the road of curiosity. If you're afraid of the unknown, you'll never discover what else there is to be revealed.

Don't hold it in

When the stress of it all just feels too heavy to carry around anymore,
gently affirm to yourself:

Today feels heavy.
Like I am burdened by all the weight
that comes with nursing.
But I have permission to cry and scream as needed
to release my frustrations. I will not feel bad about it.
I am human first. Nurse, second.

WHY THE NEED TO hold it in? Why the need to pretend it's all good? Maybe because allowing ourselves to unravel proves that we never really had it all together to begin with. I used to feel that statement so hard, but then I realized it's the farthest thing from the truth. I had to check my beliefs. Or rather, I had to put my beliefs in check. They were holding me back.

I grew up thinking emotions were bad. I watched that lack of transparency eat my mother and grandmother up alike. I watched people suffer simply because they couldn't face their own truths, much less share them with anyone else.

It's a death sentence to your spirit to hold it all in. You will implode. Growing up I believed that showing your exhaustion with life was a weakness. Even worse for my new career, I made myself believe vulnerability was a threat to this identity I was building as this nurse who had it all together. I wouldn't allow myself to break. But needing to let out some frustration doesn't mean you never had it together, it just means that somewhere along the journey it got tough and overwhelming. Maybe you feel like nobody else is crying, so you feel defeated when you need to.

But who cares what everyone else is doing? A part of self-preservation is to 'show face'. But no one ever tells us how self-destructive that can be! That true self-preservation is honoring your feelings and releasing the stress from your body so you can perform as optimally as you can. Hold on, do you even know what 'show face' is? Basically, it's when you pretend something is all good even when it's killing you on the inside. It's a lot of what we like to do on Instagram!

Sometimes you've got to close the social media tabs. Put the phone down. Wipe the makeup off. Take a long hot shower and forget the day you just had. Sometimes putting the phone down and tuning the world out makes the most sense. Because let's be really real here. When you feel like you are failing at life and you look at everyone else 'winning', it's crushing to any ounce of hope you may be holding on to. The hustle and bustle gets exhausting. You thought you had some endurance left in you, then you make the mistake of comparing your very real frustrations at the bedside to someone else on Instagram. Their staged, forced smile, the perfectly positioned stethoscope and scrubs. Sis, how did you even have time to take that picture today? And how did you look that cute with that face full of makeup while I died and came back to life just about every hour, just in time to administer meds before they were considered late? Take it from someone who also partakes in those perfectly staged photos at the bedside while you sit wondering "how sway?" Let me tell you now, those photos are in no way a true representation of how I feel or how my day went. Hell, sometimes the photo goes up on a day when I wasn't even at work! But here you are, comparing your awful day to that perfectly crafted shot.

You deserve more than to question your ability to get through a shift just because you scrolled past someone's perfectly constructed Instagram caption. And you deserve more than to be swallowed up by your frustrations. Instead, you deserve to fill the room with lavender and indulge in that glass of wine or tea or whatever you feel like. You deserve to breathe deeply and not hold your breath afraid of what the next shift will bring. You also deserve to not make an already heavy day even heavier by holding it all in.

Tears are like a valve for our stress. When your feelings reach a certain level, it signals us that emotions need to be relieved or we are going to blow. Don't judge your frustrations. Don't judge what makes you feel bad or moves you to tears. Allow those tears. Welcome them. This is coming from the girl who once cried at the dentist because I had more than one cavity and that stressed me out. Did they look at me like a weirdo? Maybe. But did I feel better? 110%. Why? Because I honored my feelings wholeheartedly. I listened to my body and respected my response to stress. When you walk around with your frustrations all tethered up into your day, your patients feel it. Your coworkers feel it. Everyone feels it, and you feel it the most; burning up inside while trying to get through a shift that is killing you. It's ok to feel overwhelmed. It's ok to not hold it together. I don't mean that you should unravel in front of your patients, but privately, it's ok. It's healthy and responsible. You are a vessel through which healing flows. You can't provide a healing environment for your patients when you haven't addressed the wounds you are carrying around. Be gentle with yourself.

Sometimes the unraveling makes us more competent. It lays down an emotional burden that creates more room for us to have empathy for those we are caring for daily. It is quite exhausting to walk around with your thoughts and feelings all caged up. You have a right to let them out. You have a right to be free of the burden of your emotions. Even with all you've sacrificed to get here and how fortunate you are to be providing care rather than being in your patient's place receiving care, you still have a right to vent. Don't let anyone strip you of your right to be human. You are allowed to complain about the frustrations of your days and weeks. You are allowed to be disappointed in how your team handled a partic- ular situation. You have a right to not feel too excited about your coworkers. Never deny yourself your humanity. Vent, but know the rules of engagement. Only vent to those you can trust. Trust here is layered. Vent only to those whom you know can be a guardian to your inner thoughts and can do so without judgment. You might be able to find people to safeguard your inner thoughts, but they may judge the hell out of you for them. No, they won't tell Sally and Nancy, but Susan is side-eyeing the hell outta you for hating your unit. Avoid venting to those who will make you feel bad for how you're feeling.

You don't need to stifle your truth. Being able to walk and talk in your truth is powerful. How you're feeling about a thing is your truth. Let it out. Get it off your chest.

Tears are a sign of strength, not weakness. It proves that you are strong enough to be vulnerable. Strong enough to admit that you are overwhelmed. Strong enough to be honest with your feelings, and that is powerful. Honesty and transparency within yourself will transform the way you interact with others. You won't feel tense trying to hold it all in. You'll flow better when you feel free from the inside out.

This journey of nursing can feel like a burden sometimes. The burden is even heavier when you think you need to carry the load alone. And even heavier than that when you are straining your neck to look around at everyone else's load or perceived lack thereof. I want you to hold onto that, 'perceived lack thereof.' We like to look like it's all together while we slowly suffer alone. The only effective way to look like nothing is burdening you is to actual do the work to unpack the load so it becomes lighter. Conserve your energy to work on lightening the load rather than trying to appear like it's not there. Deal with the issues that are stressing you out one by one, thing by thing. Is it time management? Is it calling the doctor? Is it connecting with your patients? Work on one thing every day until you've gotten comfortable with it. Then keep working on that thing until you've mastered it. The burden won't get lighter by itself over time. It will only get lighter through active effort.

We are so impressionable at the beginning. Our first experiences imprint on our hearts and form ideas about who we are as nurses and how we interact with those around us, our coworkers, and patients. If we believe that we should have it all together all the time, we begin a habit of pretending rather than being honest about our feelings and weaknesses as we learn something new. We no longer honor our vulnerability; we hide it so we don't have to face the discomfort of asking and revealing our true naivete to the team around us.

But maybe that's the burden. Pretending to have it all together and holding everything in. Maybe it's not this nursing thing. Or maybe it is but overtime we all just learn how to manage our load more effectively so we have less to pretend about. Or maybe we get stronger, so it feels lighter. Whichever way this goes, I wish you lighter days ahead. I wish you days that feel manageable. Days that feel like you've made an impact. I wish you days that feel so good that you leave the shift with no anxiety trailing behind you. Days that no longer feel like you are being weighed down, rather, days that are so uplifting you glide over any obstacles that show up. So give yourself permission to just be. Without the pressure of being anything other than what you can be in that moment. Feel what you feel. Trust what you feel. And remember your humanness when it gets too difficult.

Don't feel pressured to put the pieces back together

When you've allowed yourself the release but now you feel the pressure to pick up all your pieces,
gently affirm to yourself:

*As a new nurse, sometimes I will fall apart. I will remember
that I am not supposed to have it all together all the time.
I will remember I am not obligated to pick up
all the pieces and certainly not all at once.*

NOW THAT YOU KNOW that you don't need to hold it all in, you should also know that you don't have to pick up all the pieces all at once either. Once you drop the stuff weighing you down, you are allowed to take your time deciding what's yours and what's everyone else's. Am I anxious about this? Or am I feeding into a narrative about how I should feel? All the weight you carry around isn't always yours. So when you let it go and give yourself a chance to breathe, don't be in such a rush to pick it all back up.

This need to put ourselves back together is directly related to our need to still portray that we have it all together. You experience relief from the release then panic when you think everyone is staring and judging your process. Then you try forcing yourself to pull it together again because you start to think everyone else on your team has it all together. We start projecting our feelings and fears onto others. If we feel like we should have it all together, it's because we've created a false belief that everyone else has it all together. You would never be afraid to be vulnerable if you saw and acknowledged that others also went through a process of growth and the messy stage of learning. The problem with believing that others have it all together is that you lose your ability to discern when something is wrong and out of place with someone's work or orders. If you believe that your charge nurse has it all together all the time, will you advocate for your patient if they make an ill-fitting suggestion for your patient's plan of care? Probably not. You'll give up your right to an opinion because you'll assume that you're a big messy pile and they are a neat organized bookshelf, and so their ideas are always right. Do you see the damage? Can you recognize the rabbit hole of effects that take place when you take on the belief that you should always have it together? When you rush to put it all back together?

The beginning is for the becoming. Your becoming, no one else's. It is a growing process. It is a time to reveal all that you aren't in order to develop into all that you are. No one has it all together at first. Feeling the pressure to pretend you do is creating scar tissue. It's thickening the areas around your heart. It's removing the sensitivity and discernment you should have for your patients. It's causing you to put ego before patient outcomes, and that ain't good for anyone. So let it go. Drop all the pieces. Let them scatter. One by one, you'll pick up the things you need and leave behind the pieces you don't. When you rush to put it all back together after releasing, you'll be grabbing things not meant to come along with you on this ride. Let the pieces that no longer serve you go, and take your time as you come back together into a whole nurse who accepts that the good days are just as perfect as the bad ones.

Start over

When your soul is craving a clean slate,
gently affirm to yourself:

I give myself consent to start over.
Every day, every shift, every hour that it takes to get it right.

EVERY DAY IS ANOTHER chance to get it right. Let's get even closer. Every shift is another chance to get it right. Even closer than that; every moment is a chance to undo and do again in a way that aligns more appropriately with your spirit. You aren't tied to your past unless you want to be. So even if you did something incorrectly at 2 pm, you have another chance to fix that at 2:05 pm.

You have the right to not shackle yourself to shame. You have the right to start over as many times as it takes to get this journey you're on right. So if you need a clean slate, take it. Don't hold yourself hostage to yesterday's drama, and even more importantly, don't allow anyone else to either. You are the author of this chapter; it goes only the way you allow it to. You are the magnet attracting your experiences. If you choose to hold on to your mistakes, more mistakes will come. The universe assumes you need more because you are chilling out on that frequency. And maybe you do. Maybe you need more mistakes to show you how and where to sharpen your skillset.

But learn from the mistake. Let it teach you. Take what it's giving you to grow, and move on. Wipe the slate clean and start over. You are the creator of your experiences. If it's not going the way you want it to, fix it. You have that option. We limit ourselves. We give away our options. You don't have to live in disappointment. You can choose to learn from the moment and recreate it in so many ways that make it better. You give consent, and you take it away. The power lies within you.

So start over if you need to. Begin again from an earlier starting point if it makes the journey more palatable. Whatever you do, just remember you control how this thing goes.

Go at your own pace

When you get this crazy idea that you should know more by now;
on the days you feel stagnant,
gently affirm to yourself:

Time does not dictate my growth as a new nurse.
It tracks how long I've been doing it, not
how well I should be doing it.
I vow to not use time as a way to measure my success.

HAVE YOU EVER NOTICED how much you don't feel bothered by the time when your day is moving fast? But when you have a slow day, that clock is the most frustrating thing ever invented! Damn, is it really only 7:59? I feel like I've been here for four hours already.

We do the same thing with our careers when we feel like we should know and be learning so much more than we are. We criticize the clock. We fixate on it. But time is a poor measure of success. It's the biggest weapon we constantly use against ourselves. Why do we continue to fall victim to this inaccurate predictor of self-worth? We measure ourselves against time even in our personal lives, so I'm not surprised that we do it in our careers. I'm 30, I'm supposed to be married. I'm 25, I should have started my career already. I'm 21, I should know what I'm doing with my life already. Wrong! Wrong! Wrong! Look at how we do it at work. I've been here for six months already, I shouldn't need to ask this question anymore. I've been on this unit for 13 months, I can't seriously still not understand the pathophysiology behind this disease process. I'm the most senior nurse now, I should have already been trained and ready to be charge nurse by now.

These are such dangerous ways of thinking. Measuring your skillset against time is very problematic behavior. Just because a certain amount of time has passed does not mean you are ready for a next step and vice versa: Just because 'not enough' time has passed does not mean that you cannot take the next step yet. You could do something for 10 years and never master it, while someone else could perhaps do it after only two years. You could also be doing something for 10 years that you just aren't good at, then someone rolls onto your unit who is great at it because it is their natural strong point. Ditch the clock. Let go of the time. It's stressing you out. So what if you've been on your unit for eight months and still can't place an IV? Were you practicing IVs for eight months straight or were you running from them because you were intimidated? When you've mastered IV placement, you won't care how long you've been doing it because the only thing that will matter at that point is that you can get it done effectively. You only feel the need to compare your skills to how long you've been at a place when something is challenging for you, so you put pressure on yourself. Instead of worrying about how much time has passed, focus on how much time you put into that skill. Are you working at it persistently? Have you committed yourself to understanding all the details? Time will only frustrate you more. I also mention IVs a lot because let's face it. IVs really stress us out as new nurses. Here's a secret, there are a lot of amazing nurses who suck at IV placements. It's not necessarily a deal breaker. Your progression as a nurse should not be measured by time, but rather by understanding and skill level. Time only tracks what you've done so far, it does not dictate what you should do going forward. Never allow 'time' to distort your judgment. You can make serious mistakes if you allow time to play chess with your ego. Imagine not asking a question because you are embarrassed that you should know the answer because you've been around for a while, leading to you making a mistake that severely harms your patient. Don't our patients deserve more from us? Don't we deserve more from ourselves?

Be gentle with yourself. Time is not your gauge for how much you should know. Subscribe to measure that makes you feel good. Anything that adds pressure and isn't affecting you in a constructive way is toxic. If you're always concerned with beating the clock, you'll never be concerned with mastering your craft. You won't authentically approach your learning in a way that says, no matter how long this takes, I'll go as slow as I need to so I can absorb all the details and master this effectively. There is no other way to approach your learning.

Go at your own pace. The pace that feels healthy for you. We need more respect around our own individual processes. Our collective morale as new nurses would be a lot higher if we would honor the pace we need to accomplish things, not the invisible clock we seem to be racing against. Do you need a reminder of what's real and what's fantasy? Reality is, you're a new nurse. Delusion is, you're a new nurse who should know it all in the first year. Growth isn't some fun, painless process. And let's face it, growth does not happen all at once. There are so many experiences to be had and lessons to be learned from those experiences before you'll even get to step up a notch on this nursing belt. Stop racing against a clock that has no regard for your individuality and the way you grasp things. In the words of every New Yorker I know, "Just chhilllll!" Relax! Ditch the delusions. Come back to reality and move with a softer touch. You deserve to be as patient with yourself as you want others to be with you. Caught that? Again. You deserve to give yourself the same patience that you wish everyone at work would give you as you are trying to learn this new flow. You have your whole, entire career to get wherever it is you're in a rush to get to. So take however long you need to get to the next phase of your career, but please, leave the clock be. It's telling you nothing that will add value to your experience as a new grad nurse.

Compare only to learn

When you've committed to honoring your own pace but still fall into the comparison game,
gently affirm to yourself:

*I will use the progression of another
nurse as a means to learn,
not as a mirror I use to compare myself.*

I USED TO BE so guilty of this! I compared everything I did to the other nurses on my unit, both experienced and new nurses alike. It's like I couldn't help myself. The way the experienced nurses completed their tasks so efficiently and had time to document what they were doing. The way the physicians would laugh and joke with them. Meanwhile I was still scared to even give them an update about my patient's urine output! Oh, and God forbid the newer nurses were leaving on time and I was staying behind to finish up; I would feel so defeated. I would often ask myself, what is wrong with me? Why am I not getting the hang of this? I was exhausting myself emotionally by comparing my growth to theirs.

There was even a time when I allowed other nurses on my unit to enable that comparison game. They would point out to me how some of the other newer nurses on my unit were getting 'harder' patients, meanwhile I was still getting the easiest patients on the unit. Of course, that added pressure for me. I started resenting my assignments, thinking that everyone thought I was dumb and that's why I wasn't getting higher acuity patients.

But! Here comes the big but. I wasn't getting higher acuity patients because I never asked or expressed that I was ready to take on more. I also wasn't getting them because maybe, just maybe, my ass wasn't ready for them. Humility darling, the one thing the comparison game doesn't give you. You'll be sitting there on your high horse thinking, how come they and not me? The comparison game is unfair like that! It'll have you creating a whole story and make you mad at everyone, killing yourself for no real logical reason other than your bruised ego acting up again. Comparing yourself to others for any other purpose besides learning is demoralizing. Instead of side-eyeing my nurse friends for getting the more complex patients on my unit and cutting myself to pieces for totally made-up reasons, I could have been saying, "Hey nurse friends, what did y'all do today that allowed you to be a lot more efficient than I've been?" or "is there anything in particular that you did to be able to care for the higher acuity patients on our unit?" Or maybe I should not have been comparing myself at all because had I felt ready to take on more difficult patients, I would have started to seek the opportunity at my own pace.

You see, that's the damn problem with comparison. You'll be comparing apples to oranges and wondering why you're so upset with yourself. We each have our own unique situations and things we are overcoming every shift. It doesn't make anyone better. Our strengths are expressed in different areas. Maybe I'm great at reading rhythm strips and you great at IV placement. Newsflash, no one will learn and grow at the same pace. And just because you mastered it first doesn't mean you're a better nurse than me. If it takes me 10 months to get my first IV right and you get it on the first try, it is indicative of absolutely nothing other than you did it first. Congrats! Now teach me how so I can be great with you! That's the mentality we should have if we find ourselves comparing. Let me learn some techniques from you that will better serve our patients.

This is exactly what you should do when you compare yourself to more experienced nurses as well. They have had the time to learn how to overcome exactly what you're dealing with, and you're accusing yourself of inefficiency. Or maybe girlfriend over there you're comparing yourself to has worked as a CNA before, so even though she is new, she has a whole skillset that helps her move a bit more quickly. Comparison never works because so many variables can affect a person's performance. Compare to learn, not to destroy your nursing self-esteem. Ok? Ok!

Activity: Write your 'I Can' statements

Do you know how many times in a day we say "I can't?" We think it, we speak it, we exude it in our lack of confidence. You don't always realize how many ways you tell yourself you can't do something. It takes intentional work to remain on a higher thought frequency. We are going to get you there.

I want you to write down all the things you believe you cannot do. List them below. Then we will turn those into 'I Can' statements. This is the format for creating your own personalized affirmations. I want you to write them down on sticky notes. Then place those affirmations somewhere you can see them daily. This is how you begin to change your mindset. This is how you begin to take control of your own thought process. This is how you guide your subconscious mind into the positive realm that produces transformative physical manifestations.

Example:

'I Can't' Statement

I am not that good at placing IVs.

'I Can' Statement

I am consistently successful at placing IVs. So much so, they ask for my help on the unit.

Your turn.

'I Can't' Statements

_____

_____

_____

_____

_____

_____

_____

_____

_____

'I Can' Statements

_____

_____

_____

_____

_____

_____

_____

_____

_____

_____

Anxiety matters

When anxiety seems to be exhausting your energy,
gently affirm to yourself:

*I will remember,
the energy from my anxiety today is the same
energy that will fuel my confidence as I grow.*

DARE I SAY THIS? Anxiety is sacred to our journey as a new nurse. It reveals things to us that may otherwise go unnoticed. Would you rather know what weaknesses exist within your practice or walk around making mistakes constantly with no regard for change? It's what we do with our anxiety that makes it sacred. It's what we do with our anxiety that quells the uneasiness that comes with it. It's how we hold it up to the light and beg for it to show us the way that makes the difference. But when we ignore the anxiety, that's when it turns into a monster. It's when we want to hold on to it rather than take the lessons and send it on its way that anxiety becomes problematic.

Some days, my anxiety makes me curl up into a ball and cry. Those days are sacred too because it allows me to pause and honor the arising feelings that are overwhelming my soul. Other days, my anxiety makes me sit steadfast in the bookstore looking up the things that have been throwing me for a loop so I can be more informed. That's the key right there. Being willing to use your anxiety as a clue for what is actually bothering you. If you allow it, your anxiety can become your crutch. The thing you blame everything on. Follow the feelings. I'm anxious? Ok well what is happening right now. Oh, I need to call the doctor. Well am I prepared for this conversation? Do I know all the facts? What am I actually anxious about. You've got to go from just saying you're anxious to actually being able to pinpoint what is causing it and make a plan on how you can fix it.

No one wants anxiety, but anxiety holds a purpose. Put it to use rather than allowing it to deplete you every day. What we choose to do about anxiety is a game changer for our careers.

I never wanted to call, update, much less be seen by any physicians at work. I wanted to stay as small as possible. Me! The girl with the biggest mouth known to this planet wanted to hide. My interpretation of my anxiety was tricking me into playing small. Obliging its request was the comfortable thing to do. I knew that wasn't the right thing to do when the anxiety never went away, even after doing what I thought it wanted of me. You see, what it really needed me to do was become aware of what I needed to work on and home in on that. So I slowly started doing just that. Shift by shift, I'd speak up a bit more until I became more like myself. More assertive in my approach. More of my personality started to shine through.

If ever your anxiety calls you to do something that dims your light, that isn't the approach it wants you to take. That's your own fearful interpretation of your anxiety. There is a purpose that is bigger and bolder for you in your anxiety. Hold your anxiety as the sacred but momentary messenger it is. Let it pass by and drop off the many gems it must reveal. Then don't cling to it. Let it go.

Free yourself of its grip. Your anxiety will become more sacred to your journey as you start responding to its call for you to stand up in your light. Be that badass nurse you envisioned you'd be on graduation day rather than cringing and shying away from that discomfort you feel. Go towards it, don't run away from it.

Your power

In the moments that you find your power is slipping away, gently affirm to yourself:

> *My power is only weakened when I allow others to make me believe that I do not have it. I will trust my ability to promote healing even when the doctors, patients or other nurses do not.*

IN MY FIRST FEW months as a nurse, I was assigned to a very difficult patient for three weeks straight. Talk about burnout! He hated my being and gave me hell simply for being new and not knowing my own boundaries. He could never pull the things he did with me with anyone else because they wouldn't tolerate it. But of course, when you're new, no one tells you that you can and must have boundaries for yourself with your patients. I'd let him be as mean as he wanted as I kept a smile on my face, holding back tears I'm sure he could see. But still, I empathized with him. There he was, stuck in the hospital about to lose his leg because he could not get his diet under control, while I showed up jolly and ready to be a light to his darkness every shift. I thought I was the fairy-god nurse. This man laughed at everything I did, and not in a good way. He mocked me terribly. He would often ask me about my degree and my license as a way to demean me, as though he couldn't believe that I could pass a nursing program. After a couple of shifts with this patient, you'd wonder how you ever passed a nursing program too. Every shift with him caused me to lose a little bit of my confidence. Still, I remained soft with him. One day, he miraculously opened up to me. I still really don't know how. I almost called the doctor for a change in mental status because this man was actually trying to be nice. What was once a cold callous man now became a soft-hearted patient willing to spill his world to me. I stayed in his room for 45 minutes just listening to him. Allowing him to reach me. Hearing beyond his stubbornness and absorbing his pain. I was proud of myself. Proud of our interaction. I was proud of him! He taught me so much about the intersection of grief and anger that day. But that pride I felt quickly disappeared when I left his room. I was met with a group of furious patient care techs. Where had I been? Why did I stay in that room so long? Who did I think I was? His therapist? They tried to strip me of every honor I felt I had earned in a matter of seconds. I was so confused and annoyed at the same time! But what that patient reminded me of about myself in that moment was more than they could gave ever strip me of in their misera-bleness. This was my moment, after weeks of me trying to chisel away at my patient's stoic nature. Screw them for trying to take that away! I remembered my power. MY power. I was his thera-pist. His nurse, his therapist, his family member, his nutritionist, his waitress, his whatever he needed me to be in order for him to heal. I held power in my role as his nurse to open the door to his healing in whatever capacity.

I took psychology for a reason. I have that background for a purpose. I no longer allow anyone to have my power. Not my patients, not their families, not my coworkers, and especially no one who has never walked the road I had to walk to be here. No ma'am. Commanding a room is within my power. Choosing to sit with my patient and provide emotional support on a night shift when all my other patients are stable; that is my power. Delegating tasks to others to ensure safe and efficient care for my patients is within my power. Not allowing a patient to bully me and cross my boundaries, well that's in my power too. You see, the moment you acknowledge your power is the moment you realize that you have it to use when necessary. Your coworkers may not acknowledge it, but they will feel the power you exude, and they'll know not to play with you.

I took such an emotional beating from almost every direction as a new nurse in that first year. Most of it because I didn't acknowledge my power and I did not think I had a right to exude it. So I stuffed it in my break-room locker and forbade it from showing up with me at the bedside. That was cute until I realized how many times I was taken advantage of because I didn't operate in the strength that came with my power. Physicians communicating with me inappropriately, patient care techs telling me no when delegated to; I just about had enough before I realized that operating in my power wasn't arrogance. It was the exact confidence I worked all those years in school to develop. Showing up in my power meant using my influence responsibly. It meant knowing that I was capable of swaying the vote on a plan of care for my patient because my assessments mattered. It meant knowing that was a heavy responsibility and not taking any of it for granted.

Showing up in your power means showing up for your patients. So remember that whenever you're tempted to relinquish that power to anyone you work with. It's yours. Own it. Regard it. Hold it close to your heart and use it, because that's what you worked for.

Affirmation

I am at the bedside for a consis-
tent number of hours per shift.
I see all that comes and goes with my
patients before anyone else.
I have power.
I am aware of my power.

I hold onto my power in every diffi-
cult and easy moment alike.
I know my patient's baseline in such a perfect
way, I can sense even the slightest of changes.
I have power.
I am aware of my power.

I am a new nurse, yes, but my innocence and porosity
allow me to take on information like no one else can.
I have power.
I am aware of my power.

In my walk. In my talk. In the way I
communicate with my patients.
I am dripping with finesse.
I exude my power in everything I do. I Own it.

The doctors flock to me for answers because of it. The
families lean on me for support when they feel it.
My patients rely on me for it.
I trust my power in all ways.

Let nursing mold you

On the days when you don't feel like your absolute self, gently affirm to yourself:

I vow to always encourage and uplift the reflection in the mirror, even when it feels distorted some days.

NOT FEELING LIKE YOURSELF? Listen Linda, if you felt exactly like yourself every day on this journey then something wouldn't be right. Because nursing will pretty much strip you of every ounce of self you cling to and create a completely new you. But that's what it's supposed to do. A unique profession indeed. It causes you to challenge the parts of you that you hold on to as your identity. The parts of you that won't serve you on this new level. Maybe being quiet and withdrawn protected you before, but as a nurse, you'll need to take a step outside of that zone and speak up for your patients. You won't be allowed to be the same ol' person you were before. This journey will command the attention of every part of you that needs to rise to the occasion. It will soften the parts of you that used to be hard.

Some days you will feel defeated. It is all part of the process. Think of yourself as clay. Nursing starts to mold you into this more refined being. More compassionate, more aware of your blessings. Some pieces get smoothed out, while other parts get shaved off. Some days it'll remind you of the not-so-refined parts of yourself. The parts you hide from the world will peek out so you will be forced to deal with it. The parts of you that need to be more patient. The parts of you that need improvement. Nursing is not your sweet loving mother! She won't pacify you and blind you to your weaknesses. She won't coddle your imperfections until you accept them. She'll shove them in your face every day until you surrender to the changes needed. She is a strong force that will cause you to show up as your best self every day.

So no, every day won't feel great. You won't feel like yourself every day, but you will be growing every day. You're changing and that feels weird, but be gentle with yourself in the process. Make that vow to encourage yourself on the days you feel down. Make that vow to uphold your promise to this profession, even when it feels impossible. Make that vow to improve and love yourself through the process. Yes, some days the image looking back at you in the mirror may feel distorted. You may not recognize yourself, and the beauty in that is that you shouldn't. You should be growing and improving shift by shift. Remember, the rubber band pulls you back to catapult you forward. So even though today you might feel like 'Who the hell am I?' Day by day, you'll become more comfortable with this flower emerging from the muddy waters.

Manifest your best self

When you've been vibrating at a lower frequency than you deserve, gently affirm to yourself:

I will dare to manifest my highest potential as a new graduate nurse daily!

SOMETIMES YOU HAVE TO command what you need to show up. Dare yourself to be bold. Dare your greatness to reveal itself. Playing small serves the ego of those who don't want to see you win. It doesn't serve your growth, and it most certainly won't serve your patients. You are being introduced to the highest parts of yourself daily. Accept the challenge. Commit to waking up every day and homing in on reaching your potential. Create action steps to get there.

The first time I got an IV that no one else on my unit could get, I was ecstatic. But I had to commit to that highest version of myself before I could get there. I had to see her in the mirror every day. I had to believe she was trying to meet me and take me further. Then I had to do all the things I knew she would do. I had to take on the challenge of every IV I was tasked with rather than having someone else do it for me. I had to attempt the difficult sticks. I had to be ok with trying and failing and revamping my technique with every fail. I knew the highest version of me would accept no less, so I needed to step up to the plate at every opportunity I was allowed to do so. I had to dare myself to push past any feelings of defeat and resist the urge to be average. Because the girl who gets the IVs isn't the girl who sits around asking others to do it for her.

So command it. Own it. It's yours, but only if you want it. Ask yourself, what is it that I am trying to accomplish? What does reaching my highest potential look and feel like? What's my motivation for getting there? Sit and converse with yourself. Then command that version of you every day. Plan to show up in that version of yourself. Force that version of you to rise up. You aren't the sad, helpless newbie on the unit. You're the powerful, fresh-faced nurse ready to show up and show out in all your newness, bringing all those magical newbie vibes with you.

Activity: The expert nurse inside me

Do you ever find yourself fantasizing about what your day will feel like once you've gained more experience? I used to just doze off and imagine this popping nurse and how she would dress and feel and walk and talk around the unit. I imagined everyone gravitating to her for help. I imagined her laughing and talking with the doctor and not being so terrified of their presence.

Sometimes, it's not such a bad idea to fantasize. It allows you to create the life you want in your head first. It allows you to become really clear on what the manifestation of your goals will feel and look like.

So go ahead, make those dreams more concrete. I want you to write down what that expert nurse in you looks and feels like.

Is she/he bold and fearless?
Can he/she float to any unit and still feel as confident?
Is the expert nurse in you guiding the new grads on your unit?
Is the expert nurse in you the one everyone calls for IV placements?
Does the expert nurse in you act as charge nurse some shifts?
Is the expert nurse in you back at school for an advanced degree?

That expert nurse lives in all of us. We just need to peel back the layers until that person is revealed. We are learning and unlearning until that nurse is discovered! So speak her/him into full existence. If you were an expert today, what would that look, sound and feel like?

Write down what the expert nurse in you looks like in the most complete and descriptive way.

Baptism by fire

On the days that you are baptized by fire and not by water, gently affirm to yourself:

Some days I will learn by being gently corrected.
Other days I will learn by near drowning. It is all
still learning. I will not resent the hard lessons.

"BAPTIZED BY THE FIRE" is some random saying I heard in my childhood. Somehow it was never more relevant than when I became a nurse. All lessons aren't fun lessons. Some lessons piss you the hell off. Some lessons infuriate you. Some feel embarrassing. Some break your heart. But the one thing the lessons have in common? They teach you! They equip you with the tools you need to improve if you allow them to. Don't resent the hard lessons, because you'll miss what they are trying to reveal to you about yourself and your practice. It's sort of like a "don't shoot the messenger" kind of situation. The lessons show up so you can grow. They appear to teach you how to master your craft. You can't master something you aren't willing to confront in its fullness. That means taking the good with the bad.

As a new grad, I remember having the concept of knowing your code cart being drilled into my head. Over and over again, to the point that I started to feel like the more experienced nurses didn't want to do the tedious task of the safety checks of the code carts so they made us do it.

Until one day, my patient coded. And of course, in the adrenaline of it all, I couldn't remember which draw had what. The doctors were asking for things that my hands were shaking to find. Draw after draw I searched and scanned each thing, franticly pleading in my mind for it to show up. Oh, I was baptized by the fire that day. But you know what? I can't even be mad about that lesson. It was so absolutely necessary for me to understand the magnitude of what was being required of me. The only way I could have felt the weight of its importance was to have gone through it the way I did. It needed to show up and teach me in the most obnoxious way possible in order for me to understand that being a pediatric critical care nurse is no light task. Sometimes, the hard lessons put you right in your place and force you to pull it together. It takes that nagging little ego of yours, shoves it in the corner, and makes it shut up.

Don't resent the hard lessons. The lessons won't all politely show up and ask you your learning preference before they rip into you, but they'll all offer some valuable gems to take you through your profession. Be open to receiving those gems. Be open to the fire. Be open to the idea that like the phoenix rising from its own ashes, you'll also be stronger, smarter, and more equipped to handle the journey ahead.

Hurtful feedback

When feedback feels more painful than helpful,
gently affirm to yourself:

*I deserve constructive feedback. I deserve
words intended for me to excel.
I have the right to reject any harsh flood of words that
leave me more confused and lost than when I started.*

HAVING A COLLEAGUE GIVE you feedback can be a tricky experience. We don't always get to choose when feedback shows up. We're not always emotionally prepared for the blow to our self-esteem. But the trickiest part about feedback is that sometimes the people delivering it have zero tact in how they express their opinions. You deserve feedback, but you never deserve an attack, especially while you're vulnerable and defenseless. You're new. You're still trying to impress everyone. Let's face it, you're still trying to avoid looking stupid. You never actually look stupid, but it's a fear we hold on to and all our actions move from this place of fear.

Well, you don't have to accept mean. Stern, yes. Assertive, yes. But downright mean and disrespectful is a no. You don't need to be embarrassed in front of others and made a spectacle of to receive feedback.

Interactions like that will become draining to your motivation and to your very fragile self-esteem. Protect your spirit. You don't have to accept everyone's opinions, and you should not accept being treated with disrespect. We must be open and willing to learn, but not open and willing to be ripped apart. What others sometimes forget is that we need empathy during the feedback process. Someone to leave some room for our questions and mistakes. Someone to understand how frightened we truly are. Someone who remembers how delicate we are feeling and who will commit to handling us with the same care we handle our patients with. Don't accept from your work environment what you wouldn't accept in your home environment. Toxic is toxic, period. It's just as unhealthy in a work environment as it would be in your personal life.

The new nurse journey is overwhelming. Things move fast and your mind is stretched open with new information daily. Your obligation to learning is center stage right now, and you shouldn't be burdened by careless opinions and attitudes that make you timid during your learning. You shouldn't have to choose between self-preservation and your patient's safety. You should never have to listen to an unfounded attack on your work ethic. It's called respect. And you have a right to command it.

None of this should be confused with constructive feedback. Constructive feedback may just be difficult to hear. Sometimes criticism is tough to receive regardless of how kindly it is being offered. This isn't about constructive criticism that makes you feel a bit disappointed in your performance. This is about not accepting energy from others intended to harm you or break you down. This is about discernment. Knowing when someone is projecting on to you and knowing how to block that from absorbing into your spirit. Protecting your energy is vital to your performance as a new nurse. If you internalize the negativity that comes with certain feedback, you'll always feel insecure about that particular thing.

You have a right to only accept constructive feedback. You have the right to reject anything that causes shame or induces embarrassment. You're new, so feedback is all in the game right now. But you aren't a punching bag and don't have to take on the hurtful behaviors of others. Pray for discernment in all things. Ask the universe to guide you in what is necessary and important for your growth versus what is intended to break you down. The gift of discernment will help you in protecting your precious energy as a new nurse because you'll be able to walk away from anything weighing you down. If it feels heavy and produces shame, it's not for you. If you wouldn't repeat those words to another new grad to help them improve, then don't take it on for yourself. Remember always, you deserve constructive feedback! And you have the right to reject any harsh flood of words that leave you more confused and lost than when you started.

Constructive feedback

When constructive feedback still feels too heavy to bear, gently affirm to yourself:

Criticism will not crush me.

NOW THAT YOU UNDERSTAND how to use your discernment when feedback comes your way, you must also understand that not all criticism and feedback is bad for you. I know what it's like to think you're doing great at something only to have your preceptor or a physician, or sometimes even a patient, feel otherwise. It's crushing. It feels like a blow to your efforts. I too am a sensitive being. I don't always feel emotionally equipped to handle the words of others. But criticism is not always intended to break you. It does serve a purpose if you can see past the discomfort of having your flaws pointed out. You need professional critique from time to time to get you on your A-game. I didn't get where I was going without a few people along the way pointing out to me where they felt I needed to pull it together. In truth and with love, feedback helped me know where I needed to grow. Had I taken their feedback personally, I would not have done the necessary self-reflection I did after those conversations.

When I was in my first couple of weeks on orientation, my preceptor and I had a baby with two chest tubes under our care. We discussed the patient in detail. She watched me carry out the assessments and care for the patient, and I was feeling pretty good. My preceptor stepped away to get something, and the patient's mother came out to ask me if it was ok to change her baby's diaper. Of course, in my innocence, I told her yes. Truth be told, I don't think I was thinking about the fact that chest tubes and other delicate wires were involved and that it may not have been appropriate for a parent to change a diaper alone under these circumstances. And of course, as my luck would have it, one of the chest tubes dislodged as the mother changed the diaper. How sway? How did this manage to happen? All the emotions ran through my body. I mean all of them. I went through every stage of grief in the moments it took to settle the situation. After we carefully managed the incident with the rest of the PICU team, my preceptor pulled me to the side. Oh, the need to be pulled to the side stung like sanitizer on a paper cut. It hurt so bad; the idea that I did something wrong and negligent. I was scared and sad, and my defenses in my brain went up immediately. As soon as she tried to explain to me how this could have been avoided, all my excuses came flooding out. "But I didn't know she couldn't change the diaper." "She asked me as though she could manage." "I thought she knew to be careful." Chile, I had so much to say and I wasn't even getting in any kind of trouble. I just wasn't ready to hear "mistake" and "me" in the same sentence.

Here lies the danger. When we fear constructive feedback, we make it impossible to receive the lesson. If you can't acknowledge constructive feedback, there is no room to implement and grow from it. My preceptor was so kind and gentle. She corrected me in love and respect, but very assertively. I was shown where and how I should have intervened. I was also taught a lovely lesson on accountability in this moment. You see, this is why it is even more important not to allow others to criticize your practice without handling you carefully. Because those experiences make it difficult for you to receive the moments being sent to you with carefulness, tact, and full acknowledgment of how delicate you might be feeling. Breathe through the discomfort of the moment. Let your guard down, and allow yourself to hear what is actually being said to you. No excuses, no fear, just be open and ready to accept a teaching moment. So remind yourself often: the criticism will not crush me. It can propel me into the best version of my nursing self if I am open to receiving it and willing to use it wisely.

Activity: Create a list of criticisms

When was the last time you acknowledged criticism you received? When was the last time you actually heard it instead of getting caught up in the fact that someone had the audacity to check you? I know it's easy to throw a temper tantrum with our close friends and family when someone offers us some unsolicited words of wisdom, but when was the last time you actually dissected the feedback? I know some things are not offered to us in a neatly tied package, but does that mean we should ignore it? Does it mean we should write those people off as haters?

Not every critique given to you should be ignored. Even if Sally had the worst attitude when she told you that double-checking your medication before giving it was super important, you should still acknowledge that there is a strong possibility that what Sally said does in fact apply to you. Ignore Sally's attitude and tone. That part is not your business. What is your business is determining if what she said actually applies. Because growth happens at every corner. A sure sign you are growing is when you can dismiss the negativity in someone's comment and still find the light in their darkness.

Growth isn't easy. Lessons don't always come neatly wrapped. Sometimes they are sloppy and mean. Sometimes the person giving the advice is uncouth and deserves to be put in their place, but then you'll lose. You won't grow. You won't know where and how you need to grow. Their hard delivery is a reflection of their stunted growth. Your gracefulness in receiving their advice anyway is how you'll flourish. Learn how to isolate the information being given to you and leave your emotions at the door.

Write down the most recent criticism you received at work. Also write down any recurring pieces of criticism you've received. Write them all down. Whether you thought them of yourself or they were offered to you by your manager, physician, or coworker. Write them all down below. Then ask yourself, "Does this truly apply to me?" for each one. If it does, place a check mark next to it. This process takes a lot of tough love, honesty, and true reflection. Once you've gone through each piece of criticism, create a plan to deal with them. How are you going to actively work on this area needing improvement on your end? Make an action plan so you can hold yourself accountable. Then begin to implement each plan day by day. Be patient with yourself. Take the most important item on the list and start there. Anything dealing with practicing safely should be addressed first. Then go through the list week by week until you feel the difference in your flow. You have to get so in tune with yourself as a nurse that you feel the difference in when things are flowing and when they are stagnant.

_____

_____

_____

_____

_____

_____

_____

_____

_____

_____

Stay soft

On the days when you feel the innocence of this journey leaving you and a tough exterior is showing up in its place, gently affirm to yourself:

I will remain soft.
Even though working as a new nurse
is one of the hardest things I have ever done.

THINK OF A ROSE. Even with thorns running down its stem, the flower itself still remains soft. It retains its beauty and elegance even in the setting of a stem full of thorns.

Nursing is not just one of those careers you can skate through and leave with no scars. Nursing has so many hard days. Some are full of joy, others make you want to scream and yell at everything moving. The blessing is in finding your patience and retaining your softness when everything is upside down. Your patients need the soft you. The one who hears the pain under every "I'm ok". They need the nurse who can still hold their hand after they made your day hell. They need the nurse who will go find the last sandwich on the other units late at night even when they refused to order dinner before the kitchen closed. The soft you is the healer. The soft you is the one who shows your patients that you believe in them so they have permission to believe in themselves.

Even though it can be a challenge, relax into the softer you. Forgive the frustrations that bubble up when the day is overwhelming. Forgive yourself for the way you rushed your patient's story during your morning assessment because your head was so full of every other responsibility. Forgive yourself and release the tension that comes with your aggravation. When you can be gentle with yourself, your patients will feel the extension of that self-love. Sometimes we harden as part of our defense mechanism. And trust me, I understand that. It's a scary world, starting out in nursing. All these personalities, all these diagnoses, all these difficult families, and here you are, raw and naked, trying to learn. It makes sense that your guard would go up. But while you defend against the newness of the process to protect yourself, you also defend against the possibility of connecting with your patients. You're also warding off the nurses who want to help you and be true allies. Vulnerability is scary, but only through that authenticity will you truly be able to connect to the heart of your work. So even though some days you want to bring that tough exterior, know that sometimes it's essential to take off the armor and allow your softer side to prevail.

Be diligent

When you're feeling overwhelmed and your work begins to suffer, gently affirm to yourself:

I will remember that foresight is better than hindsight. Especially when someone else is counting on my judgment. I vow to remain diligent in my work even on the days when I am overwhelmed.

HAVE YOU EVER WORKED with a personal trainer? No? Don't! They'll work you to the bone! More importantly, you'll never get away with bad form because they'll always value quality over quantity. They'd rather you do two perfect push-ups that work the correct muscle groups than 20 sloppy push-ups that put you at risk of injury. They force perfection out of you even when you're tired and overwhelmed.

This is the same diligence we must have as new nurses. I'd rather you be late with some meds if it means you properly assessed your patient, notified the doctor of your concerns, and got some new orders implemented to avoid any worsening of your patient's condition. When you're working as a nurse, your foresight is so important to the well-being of your patient. You must see something before they even know it's a possibility. You must walk into a room and see that the commode is just two inches too far for your patient to reach, understanding that it will cause a fall and fixing it rather than walking in on that fall because you did not do an efficient safety check of your room because you were rushed. Your ability to understand the repercussions of an action can help you become a stronger nurse.

But do remember, you need insight in order to have foresight. You need to understand your patient population. You need to know the assessments that are needed for the diagnoses you commonly see. How can you have foresight for an asthmatic when you aren't checking breath sounds? How can you prevent further decompensation if you don't have the knowledge that a prolonged expiratory phase in the setting of wheezing means they are still in an acute phase and need albuterol often? How can you stop this patient from requiring further respiratory support and declining if you don't know what to look for?

Remember, foresight is better than hindsight, but foresight requires insight first. Be diligent about your assessments and the things you implement. They say hindsight is 20/20, but foresight can be 20/20 too if we choose to be meticulous about everything we do at the bedside. Don't look back and "shoulda, coulda, woulda" something that was avoidable with just a bit more of your focus and attention. Quality will always be better than quantity. Take your time understanding each and every step. Slow down and work more diligently. With each moment that you take action, you are building your judgment. The ability to see and know what will happen next if you don't intervene. But if you're rushing through the moments, you miss the small details that might be hinting at something more. Take your time with the lives of your patients. Don't underestimate the fact that they are relying on your knowledge to take them through another critical hour.

Ask all the questions

When your need to ask more questions is making you uncomfortable,
gently affirm to yourself:

Today I may ask a million questions,
but one day I will be guiding another nurse's
uncertainty with answers.

IMAGINE BEING AFRAID TO ask someone the very question your patient turns around and asks you. Ha! There is nothing more uncomfortable than to stand between a patient and their Google search and you have no sensible answer because your ego told you it was better to not ask that last question.

I used to hate asking questions. Until I realized how much more uncomfortable it was to sit in the unknown all by my lonesome because I was too scared or proud to ask about something I didn't understand. A part of growth is asking about the things you need clarity on. Wait, forget growth. A part of your obligation to your patients and your profession is to ask as many questions as necessary to safely care for your patient population.

Questions can be intimidating, especially when directed towards the wrong people. Let me explain. When I first started as a new nurse, there was one nurse in particular that I would never ask or direct any questions to. I wouldn't even dare ask where the bathroom was. I eventually realized it wasn't beneficial to me to stifle my questions, but I also knew that my self-esteem had been bruised one too many times from asking this one particular nurse anything. She always had a snarky response. Like girl, just answer the question! I had to stop asking that nurse questions because she was creating insecurities for me around a very necessary part of my job. I had to find the people who were gentle enough for my fragile spirit at that time; who never deflected in a mean way. You have to find your people on your unit. The ones who you feel safe with. The people who won't perpetuate your insecurities. A colleague or two whom you can trust. Because it's very possible you might have a million and one questions. Find yourself some people who won't mind answering a million and two of those questions for you.

Use your resources

Let me give it to you another way.
When you become insecure around your need to ask,
gently affirm to yourself:

A smart nurse is not one who knows all the answers,
but one who knows how to find all the answers.
I promise to always use my resources
and never be too proud to ask for help.

BEFORE I STARTED MY first travel assignment, an amazing traveler that I worked with gave me this sound advice. She said, you're a smart girl, but you don't have to remember it all at any given time. Being a smart nurse is about knowing how to find all the answers, not knowing all the answers. Ahhhh! My life was changed. The pressure gone! You mean to tell me I don't need to retain every ounce of information at all times? Nope girl, you don't.

I used to feel embarrassed asking for help about some things. I would go back and forth in my head 10 different times about how I would ask and if I should ask at all. I would walk up to people but lose my guts to ask and then walk away. I hated the idea of help. Until I realized I was putting my own judgment of myself into the mouths of others. No one had a problem helping me or answering any of my questions. I had the problem. All by myself. I was projecting.

But the catch to all of this is that getting help doesn't necessarily mean getting it from other nurses. Knowing how to use my resources meant opening a reference book. It meant calling pharmacy for a question they were experts on. It meant looking at the policies and procedures book for my unit. YouTube is also filled with gems. And with all these other places to find help, you can still ask your nursing colleagues. But you don't have to come to your colleagues fully blind. You can pull up just a bit visually impaired. What do I mean? Some of your questions can come with some of what you do know versus showing up with a fully loaded question with no display of your background knowledge. Hey Sally, I know when we draw labs we "xyz", but what happens after that? Versus hey Sally, how do we draw labs again? You see how different that was?

Always remember, a smart nurse is one who always knows how to find answers and is not afraid to go looking. The only dumb question that exists is the one you don't ask because you're embarrassed.

Delegation is your friend

When you need to get it done, but you're afraid to send for help, gently affirm to yourself:

Delegating will not intimidate me.
It will empower me to use my resources to enhance my abil-
ity to safely and effectively care for my patients. It is a true
reflection of my self-awareness to know when I need help.

DO YOU HAVE AN extra set of hands that magically grow out your arms when you arrive at work? Trick question. Because the answer is yes. Yes, in fact you do. They only activate when you use this magical tool called delegation. It's actually my favorite topic but can be quite intimidating for new nurses. It's right up there with calling the doctor at 2 am for meds you forgot to ask for at the reasonable hour of 8 pm.

Most new nurses don't delegate enough. It's as though we think that asking others for their help makes us incompetent. Safely delegating is a very necessary part of our job description. In fact, you can do more harm to your patients by not delegating when you should. Let this sink in now. You cannot and must not do it all. This is impossible, although we try almost every shift. Asking your patient care tech or certified nursing assistant to get a set of vitals while you go grab and double-check your medication before administration is absolutely acceptable, and you should never feel bad about it. When you delegate effectively, you increase your productivity. But I should also mention that I am a huge advocate for completing some tasks that you know are part of your PCT or CNA's tasks for the shift if you can. No sweat to empty a foley if you're in a room and see it's getting full. Teamwork is the name of the game.

I know that delegating can feel like a challenge. You're new; how can this new person here think they can just tell anyone what they need? That's the story you feed yourself. That you're new and should shut your mouth and do it all alone. Rather than getting to know the folks you will eventually need to delegate to and offering them some help from time to time, we ignore their ability and responsibility to help. I'm giving you some tough talk here, but I sympathize. Especially when the ones you're delegating to have been on the unit since before nursing school was even a thought for you. It's hard yes, but does the new physician hesitate to put in those orders for you to complete any tasks needed for the patients they are caring for? Didn't think so. That resident walks right up to you and tells you the 10 incorrect orders they just placed all proud and happy too. So why should you hesitate to ask for vitals or a diaper change or any of those things that you need to more effectively care for the patients you're assigned to? If you don't delegate a task, you'll still have to answer to someone about why that thing wasn't done. Not having had time is not an answer anyone accepts, no matter how true that may be. Not only do you answer to the powers that be, you have to answer to your own moral compass at the end of the shift when your fear of asking for help got in the way of the best possible outcomes for your patients.

Is it really worth it to do it all alone if it means compromising on the quality of care you can provide? Didn't think so.

Start developing a rapport with those you must delegate to. Start introducing yourself to them. Start offering a helping hand where you can to ease the burden of that awkward delegating moment. Whatever it is you need to do to grow more comfortable with your coworkers, get to it. Delegating actually empowers you and your patients. Imagine having your patient hold their urine because you're afraid to ask your tech or colleague to run next door and help them, and they have an accident? That is demoralizing for your patient. It's also ruining the integrity of your work when you have to rush what you're doing to get next door, easily leaving room for mistakes. But what if that isn't the worst that could happen? Imagine your patient urinates on themselves or falls rushing to the toilet because you left them waiting, and now you have a disaster on your hands. Now you've lost their trust. Now they feel embarrassed. Now the family is upset. It's an awful sequence of events that I've seen take place that could be avoided by exercising your right to delegate.

However you go about it, delegating is non-negotiable. It's how we all work as a team to provide the highest level of healing for our patients. So feel empowered to practice using it! It's a necessary part of the job. Stop talking yourself out of doing it. Stop rationalizing the very irrational excuses you're giving yourself about why you can do it all alone. We are all fingers on a hand. Everyone has to pull their weight. If the thumb tries to over-compensate for the index finger, the thumb compromises the whole integrity of the hand if it over exerts itself and becomes injured. You are doing the same when you attempt to do it all alone. You're burning yourself out. Doing a disservice to your patients and the plan of care for them in the process. Think of delegating as being an even better team player. Committing to not doing it all is indeed making the team stronger. You are recognizing and acknowledging your limitations and not slowing your team down. You're passing the tasks on to the appropriate member so you can stay operating in your genius zone as the nurse. You are staying in your magic when you comfortably delegate when appropriate. Be gentle with yourself and your teammates in the process, but get it done. No more compromises on this one. Delegating is part of how we show up fully for our patients.

Honor your process

When your learning process seems to embarrass you, gently affirm to yourself:

I will respect the way I learn.
I (insert your name) will honor my process and respect
the way I incorporate information into my practice.

STOP LETTING OTHER PEOPLE drag you into their hole of shame. The only reason why we want to reject parts of ourselves is because we feel judged and want to assimilate to the norm of the environment we are in. That's a trap. Wanting to do things how someone else is doing it and ignoring your special way of doing, is one big ol' trap. Your perspective is powerful. The way you show up as a nurse is to be revered. That includes the way you learn. The way you learn and process information should be honored and held on a pedestal. It's your process! Just hear me dragging the word "your" out. Youurr process. It's no one else's to understand; only to be respected! I want you to stop feeling guilty about the fact that you might be a person who needs to write down the steps to a procedure and read it over a few times for you to execute it effectively. Stand firm in the learner that you are and advocate for your needs. Don't be guilted out of needing to be hands-on for a task while someone is explaining the steps in order for you to safely do it alone the next time. Your learning process is your guarantee. Honoring your process is ensuring your comfort and confidence in being able to perform safely as a nurse at all times. And, it's how you got right here to this place. You passed nursing school with that process. You studied and passed the NCLEX with that process. It's not failed you yet, so why let others shame the way you approach this new journey?

We need to become more assertive about our needs as new nurses. If being hands-on is more beneficial, then advocate for more moments of doing. If understanding the reasoning behind a skill helps you perform that skill better and retain the technique in your mind better, then ask for a more detailed explanation. There is no pity party to be had for how you choose to get things done. Those are your unique gifts that help you excel. It's your unique way of seeing this nursing thing. Do you know how many different ways one can calculate a dose in med math? I remember as a new nurse, a colleague really wanting to show me how to do a dosage calculation their way. But I didn't like their way. It felt complex, it wasn't intuitive to my brain, and I feared that I would make too many mistakes attempting that way. Funny enough, they hated my way too. She just didn't understand how my brain could do it the other way when she felt her way was easier. Guess what? We both used a different technique to get to the same answer. Does it really matter in the end that I prefer my way and you yours? Do I really need to convince you that my way is better? No. I don't. I calculate med dosages in the way that feels like a comfortable and easy method for me. My brain and body prefer this way and I don't need to convince you or anyone else why. We just gon' respect the way I do my math and move on. So long as our individual ways are proven to give a consistently correct answer, you do you boo and I'm gonna do me.

This is the stance I want you to have when it comes to your learning process. Honor your way. Be open to new ways but ultimately rest on the techniques that feel good to you. I, for one, need an explanation for everything. I need to understand it before I am able to execute it alone. That's just how I remember. When I understand how a thing works, I am able to think through the moments I feel stuck. I can't feel confident in a procedure if I don't understand the rationale behind why we do. Once I know the reasoning, I can synthesize all steps in my head even when the pressure is heavy in a moment, and even if I haven't done it in a while. I know why so I'll remember how. That's just my way. Do you know how many times I've gotten eyes rolled at me because I needed an explanation? Yes Sally, please explain to me why and don't just show me the steps. Tell me why those steps. Hell, half the time the eye rolling was probably because the person I was asking had no idea why and they do it robotically themselves. Imagine I let that person discourage my process? I would be another nurse setting herself up for failure and major errors.

Honor the way you get things done and never feel ashamed about your process on this journey. If it's safe, if it feels comfortable, if it doesn't violate any policies, then it's yours to keep for however long you need it. Capeesh?

Beyond your stethoscope

When your stethoscope frightens you,
gently affirm to yourself:

This is my stethoscope.
I vow to recognize and understand its power
to help me in situations where its information
is needed to intervene.
I vow to use it as a tool to enhance my
knowledge of my patient and not as one of intimidation.

MY FIRST STETHOSCOPE WAS a teal, double-tubing, no-name stetho-scope I found in the bookstore of my nursing school. Lord bless that terrible piece of rubber, and may no student be unfortunate enough to pay $29.99 for another one ever again. Because that thing was crap. I could not hear a single thing through it. It muffled every sound coming back to the earpiece and left me looking at my clinical instructor with a look of fear.

My stethoscope betrayed me those years. It was as though I expected it to whisper what I was hearing back to me. I wanted it to transmit and interpret sounds for me. Was I really asking for too much?

I soon realized that the double-tubing stethoscope was intended for episodes of fake doctor shows and traded it in for one that would actually work. I bought a beautiful new black single-tubing stethoscope for $150 once I realized that the teal one was going to make me fail nursing school.

But that's when it hit me. All these stethoscopes were useless unless I became useful. Because the $150 brand name did me no better than the bookstore no-name one. It gave me better sound transmittance, but ya girl still needed to know what the heck she was hearing. I needed to have autonomy over the tool and stop allowing it to intimidate me. I needed to gain power over it. This tool was there to give me insight on what was happening with my patient. That's it. Nothing more and nothing less. It was just another piece of the puzzle.

We allow the tools at work to intimidate us because we are unfamiliar with its use. The pool looks deep until you hop in and feel the bottom. You've got to get used to hopping in and getting familiar with all the unknowns at work. I started to use my stetho-scope to listen to everyone I knew, even my dog. I started asking to listen to other nurses' patients. I needed to first get comfortable with the normal so I could easily identify the abnormal. Then I committed to taking it a step up. I wanted to identify each abnor-mal sound for what it was. Is it a murmur? Is it crackles? I stopped letting this piece of metal and plastic scare me and started letting it empower me!

Then I went further with my knowledge. I became commit-ted to identifying the necessary interventions, if any, for each abnormality. I committed to steps that would improve my prac-tice as a nurse. But it all started with a mindset change around my stethoscope. I had to stop telling myself that I was afraid of it simply because I needed more practice around the insight it was giving me. Every unknown isn't the death of you. Sometimes it's an invitation to learn more. Do you run from the new kid at school because you don't know them? Hopefully not. You walk up to them and get to know more about them. Your stethoscope is welcoming you to do the same with it and with your patients. It is facilitating better patient care by helping you hear what is on the inside of the 84-year-old CHF patient in room 39.

These days, the stethoscope and I are friends again. It still isn't interpreting things for me, but we're getting along well. Do the same for yourself this week. Demystify all the equipment in your work environment that intimidates you. Allow it to empower your practice as a nurse by changing your mindset around it and committing to touching, feeling, and using it. Make this vow to yourself. "I vow to use my stethoscope frequently to assess and reassess, not just as an accessory to my uniform. I vow to recognize and understand its power to help me in situations where its information is needed to intervene. I vow to know when the sounds I hear with it are abnormal even if I do not know what the sound I am hearing is. I vow to keep it on my person and not as a decoration for my locker, car mirror, or a tool to get me out of traffic violations. I vow to use it as a reminder that I am a novice nurse and I will not harshly judge my performance every shift but rather embrace the fact that my journey of never-ending learning has just begun."

You come first

When advocating for everyone else feels easier than standing up for yourself,
gently affirm to yourself:

> *I will learn how to advocate for myself*
> *before I advocate for my patients. I under-*
> *stand that for my patients to trust me to meet*
> *their needs, my needs must first be met.*

I'M PRETTY SURE WE'VE all heard that you can't pour from an empty cup. So I'll skip that approach, because you know this. Let me just remind you of the disservice you do to your patients when you are afraid to stand up for yourself. When you take dignity away from yourself, how will you know how to empower your patient in difficult moments? The authenticity is missing.

Standing up for yourself automatically gives way to a better experience for your patient. Forcing yourself to show up to work when you're sick because the census was high gives your patients the worst of you. Running around all day with an assignment you're unfairly drowning in without telling your charge nurse can cause you to miss details that could be important in preventing your patient's decline. I want to insert the clapping hands emoji right here. You don't owe it to anyone to give what you don't have.

More importantly, you cannot give what you don't have. So speak up for yourself. Create healthy boundaries. Without boundaries you'll become burnt-out. And a burnt-out nurse isn't giving their best to their anyone. Master self-advocacy, which in turn leads to better patient advocacy. They're cutting your orientation short because they are short staffed? ISSA NO! Every time you allow an injustice in your practice, you get more complacent about them. Every time you're unwilling to say no to something that doesn't feel safe to you, you're making it easy to not question the actual unsafe things. Every opportunity you're presented with is practice for the bigger themes that may arise. How could I feel comfortable sharing my patient's concern about discharge when I don't even feel comfortable about sharing my own discomfort around the fact that it's 1 pm and I still haven't had a breakfast break? You have to give so much of yourself in 12.5 hours. It's the nature of the profession. So don't show up and let everyone take from you without creating healthy work boundaries. No Sally, I don't want to go to break at 5.30 pm today. I did that yesterday and it's unhealthy. No Nancy, I ain't coming in with a cold and wearing a mask and running myself into the ground because you got three admissions overnight. Insert clapping hands emoji again. Learn how to advocate for yourself. It's how you set the foundation for a thriving career and ease the potential for burnout. No one feels more burnt-out than a new grad nurse who says yes to everything that is too heavy to say no to. Become an advocate for yourself before you're pulled in so many directions you're pulled apart. "No" is normal. "No" is healthy. "No" is honoring your personal and professional boundaries. And you have a right to your "No" just as much as everyone else.

Certainty is a must

When you're feeling unsure but feel forced to push ahead anyway, gently affirm to yourself:

I promise to never complete a task with lingering uncertainty because my ego advised me otherwise. I owe it to my patients to ease the doubt and confusion first.

RULE OF THUMB, NEVER allow your ego to lead the way at work. Actually, never give it the lead anywhere, but especially when you're responsible for facilitating someone's healing. Be discerning. Ego will always steer you away from asking questions because it wants to feel right. It wants to feel protected. Ego will always make you give the needy patient an attitude because how dare someone take away time from your own personal agenda? Ego will always advocate for the fear-induced response. It stays far away from humility. Ego makes you think you know it all, and why the hell would you ever need to ask?

Never ever trust the ego, especially when caring for the lives of others. Ego in the toxic sense, that is, as we discussed earlier.

When working, you should always address any lingering uncertainty you might feel. Never push through a red flag. That becomes dangerous to your practice. No matter how far you've gotten into a thing, always stop for clarity. That could mean stopping right before you push a pain med with a screaming patient to review the dose and make sure it's correct. It could mean double-checking when you're peacefully about to walk out the elevator but are unsure if you documented that urine output that the team has been waiting on for over 10 hours.

Of course, pushing past all your alarm systems is easier than having your head chewed off because you stopped to validate some information. Running out the door to your car feels much more tempting than turning around to double-check. None is above the other. An uncertainty is an uncertainty, and we owe it to our patients to be clear as day about everything that involves their care. Part of our obligation to caring for the lives of others is to be thorough. Reading the order completely, not scanning a few words that could change the entire intent of the message.

My first lesson in being thorough started with nursing school. I'm a scanner when I read questions. I would scan and always miss the not. So instead of reading, "What would not make this a complete lab order?" I would read, "What would make this a complete lab order?", and choose the wrong answer. Classic. It bit me in my butt enough times that I started reading every word.

Take pride in being thorough. Take pride in clarifying things that you feel hesitant about. Take pride in sharpening your practice. It's why, even in a code, we do a callback of the order out loud. Because no moment is above your need to make sure it is correct and safe. Trust me, you'll sleep better at night.

Be open to learning

When being taught a new thing feels disruptive to the routine you desperately cling to,
gently affirm to yourself:

*I will remain open to all the lessons my nursing journey
is trying to reveal to me.
At all times, not just in the beginning,
I will remain pliable and
approachable enough to be taught.*

DO YOU KNOW WHY people stop growing and progressing in their careers and lives? Because they choose to. Every time you are unwilling to be taught, you're choosing to remain stagnant. Every time you think your way is better and you aren't open to another possibly more efficient way, you choose to remain stagnant. This is not to be confused with wholeheartedly honoring your process. Honoring your process also means "I am open to seeing if there is another more efficient way that feels comfortable to me." You can be open to learning while still honoring YOUR way of doing things.

The comfort of routine has been killing growth since before time. This growth thing is a choice. A consistent and intentional choice. Choose to grow every damn day! Not just in your journey as a nurse, but in your journey as a person. Remaining open to growth is the surest way to allow the lessons to find you. Nothing knocks at a locked door for too long. Your lessons don't have time to convince you that you need them.

The single most humbling decision of my life was becoming a travel nurse. It forced me to open up to other ways of doing things. Other ways of communicating and being. It gave me an opportunity to show up as a softer Jannel. It forced me to have to be taught the same thing over and over again in multiple ways to that hospital's liking. It showed me that there were other, more efficient ways of approaching this nursing thing and that if I clung to my way simply because it was all I knew, I would never see the infinite opportunities that exist to be a better nurse for my patients. It showed me that being stubborn would get me nowhere but out the door.

Many years in and I'm still intrigued by all that I learn, because I choose to remain open to it. We all know that nurse who's been doing a thing since before we were born and is stubborn about seeing and using any other method. Not that their way helps them practice more safely, but only because they don't want to step out of their comfort zone. While I will agree some of those methods are genius, some are plain and simple outdated by evidence-based practice.

We must be willing to be taught new things. We must be willing to be corrected on old things. Remaining open to correction ensures that you are consistently operating in the best interest of your patient. Imagine no one wanting to correct you about your technique because you're never receptive. Imagine making an avoidable mistake because no one wants to tell you anything. Imagine the manager needing to pull you aside because of that avoidable mistake. Exactly. It ain't cute, and it ain't warranted.

Stay open. Stay pliable. Remain flexible. Remain adaptable. That is what it means to be a nurse.

Activity: List your weaknesses

Where do you struggle? What are you embarrassed to reveal you need help with? Write them down here as a way of acknowledging the things that need improvement and commit to improving in those areas. Then write out your plan for improving each of those things. It's one thing to acknowledge where you need help and another to be intentional and realistic about how that gets done.

_____

_____

_____

_____

_____

_____

_____

_____

_____

_____

_____

_____

_____

Freedom from pride

When your ego wants to follow you in for your shift,
gently affirm to yourself:

*Humility sparks a better response than ego ever could.
I will check my attitude at the door.
Especially with my patients.*

I AM HITTING THIS concept of ego from every angle in this book. I
searched the Internet long and hard for a definition of humility
that would drive home my point here. I found one, and it resonated
perfectly. The definition of humility I saw as it relates to the new
nurse experience is "freedom from pride." I love that! Those words
are so relevant. You see, it's the refining part of nursing we don't
want to talk about. The pruning that takes place that we want to
sweep under the rug.

Freedom from pride means not allowing your ego to trick you
into a back and forth with your patients. It means not pretending
you know something you don't. It means asking for help when
you need it, even if the nurse who will help you can be annoying.
It means setting your ego aside to benefit your team. It means
swallowing any word vomit that may hinder you from forming a

therapeutic relationship with your patients. You see, we've talked about confidence and the natural feelings that come with being new in this book, but have we sufficiently discussed how much your ego will spill over into your work life? How some days it'll feel better to slip some attitude in when talking with folks who've consistently been rude rather than back down? Have we discussed how some patients will question your right to be there and how you'll have to bite your tongue to ensure their comfort over yours? That's the part of nursing no one talks about. The growing up you have to do. The maturation in your spirit. Do you know how much growing it took for me to not have a rebuttal every time my patient had something nasty to say? Oh, it took a lot of "Forgive them Father for they know not what they do or who they are playing with" moments. I had to become very clear on my triggers, or everything at work would become triggering for me. I had to identify the feelings I felt in every moment so I could respond out of love and kindness, free from my pride.

If you carry your pride with you every day, you'll win some battles, but you'll lose the war for sure. Trust me, I've been there and done that, and no response would ever justify the guilt I would feel when I led with my ego. Become aware of yourself as a person and you'll be that much more aware of yourself as a nurse. What motivates you? How do you stay disciplined? What questions trigger an insecurity within you? What tone within a person triggers an annoyance within you?

I don't like authoritative figures. I had to learn that about myself. I grew up in a very authoritative environment. Do this, do that. I had to learn within myself that certain leadership styles weren't going to do well with me. I need to feel my autonomy. I need to feel collaborative. Most nurses desire that. But I had to learn that this would be a personal trigger for me when being "told" what to do. I perform better when I feel respected and appreciated; when I am asked about the timing of my day rather than having things shoved at me.

I understand myself as a nurse. With that understanding came responsibility and awareness. When a charge nurse came to me and it felt like they were going to tell me how to manage my patients, I recognized that the situation might feel bigger to me than the actual moment, so I needed to listen to what was being suggested rather than allow my ego to shut that charge nurse out. When a patient's parent wants to change a diaper at 8:17 pm every night and they tell me that's what I'll be doing, I had to learn how to surrender to the moments rather than fight them. No attitude, no irritation. Just me understanding that it was triggering for me and controlling the emotions that came up.

Being a nurse isn't some concrete, follow the rules perfectly and go home kind of profession. It's abstract. It pulls on every part of you and demands better from you every shift. It won't allow the outdated version of you to hang around. It demands your upgrade. Grow with it. Get curious about the new you that is being challenged to emerge.

Know who you are

When the whispers of your weaknesses get louder, gently affirm to yourself:

> *No one can convince me that I am a bad nurse,*
> *unless I already believe it.*
> *I will change my mindset around my abilities.*

WRITE DOWN YOUR NAME on a piece of paper right now. Look at it. Say it out loud. Do you sense the knowingness you feel when you hear your own name? You know it's you, right? If someone calls you, you will look. If you see your name on a check for a million dollars, you'll know without a doubt that it's yours, right?

Let me go deeper. When people say "Beautiful" or "Pretty Girl" from across the room, I always instinctively look to see who is calling me. Why? Because I have made an agreement with my spirit that those things are true. When people tell me how smart I am, I can almost hear my mind respond with, "I know". Now let's go even deeper. If I called you by another name that wasn't a nickname you agreed to, would you respond? Would you turn around? In fact, if you even had an inkling I was trying to get your attention with a wrong name, you would correct me, wouldn't you?

When the patient asks if you're the doctor or the CNA, don't you proudly correct them with your nursing title?

That patient can't convince you that your title is something else or that you went to school for something else, could they? Then why is it that a couple of bad days and challenging encounters have convinced you so easily that you're not good at this? Is it because you have already convinced yourself that you suck? No one can easily change your mind about something you haven't already partially agreed to on the inside. This is why you need to get firm and unapologetic about who you are and what you came to do. I know who I am as a nurse, so a couple of bad days can't convince me otherwise. I know all the battles I fought to get to this very moment, so a rude doctor ain't gonna make me throw in the towel. I know the lives I came to touch with these healing hands, so a patient throwing some mean words at me won't deter me from my purpose.

You have to get crystal clear on who you are and what you came to do, or you'll leave everything and everyone else to dictate that for you. I don't give anyone the power to tell me who I am. I spent too much time with myself growing, reflecting, and overcoming to allow one bad situation to turn that upside down. You have got to get so confident in your ability to grow and expand that you start looking folks in the face like maybe it's you and not me. Stop giving people authority over your self-esteem. Take their privileges to your life back. Say no more! I know who I am and what I came to do, so even if it doesn't look pretty today, it'll get there. Even if you can't see the potential in my walk because I am stumbling right now, just know I am getting ready to run circles around you on this unit.

I need you to have the audacity to believe that you came to fulfill a purpose even when you haven't found the purpose yet.

Don't give anyone permission to make you feel small or under-qualified. Yes, I came to learn from you, but no, I didn't come to be berated by you.

Set and hold your boundaries. Set and hold your beliefs about yourself. Remember who you are at all times and no one, absolutely no one, can convince you of anything else.

I remember when I quit my first job. After a horrible four months, I knew it was a wrap. I confidently told them I was out of there and on my way to a Pediatric ICU. A PICU that was ranked in specialties and regularly featured in the media. I was leaving y'all ungrateful asses and going where I would be celebrated. Oh baby, they had so much to say. I get why. My career wasn't looking too promising there. I wasn't learning fast enough according to my preceptor. But I knew I was a fast learner. According to them, I was behaving like a robot with my patients, but I knew I was a congenial person. I was confused about who I was for a while.

But then I messed around for a bit and remembered. You see, people don't like when you remember how golden and special you are. I had forgotten my name, but enough was enough, and I started to remember. I got the hell out of there. They weren't nurturing who I was. They were causing me to forget. They started to convince me that I sucked because in all reality, I walked in there subconsciously thinking that.

Stop thinking that because you're new to a field you suck. You were divinely created and set aside for a special purpose. If you walked into the room for it, it's because someone believed that with the right training you would be a master at it. And that someone better be you. So never forget who you are. Never allow people around you who only remind you of your weaknesses. Surround yourself with people who glorify your strengths, and use them to improve your weaknesses. So yeah, I handed that resignation letter in like the badass I remembered I was. I started believing I was worth a better environment to work in, and I got it. I started surrounding myself with nurses who believed I was great, and I was assigned to a preceptor who helped me walk in my light. I started to change my mindset, and everything I believed I deserved showed up around me.

Stand up in who you are and force everyone around you to do the same. Your environment will only reflect what you believe is possible deep down inside!

Activity: Letter to my future nursing self

I have been you. On some days, I still am you. I want to encourage you to reach for the abundance that is awaiting you. Sometimes, as we grow, we don't always feel anything good, so we mistake it for moving backwards or stagnation. But baby, those growth pains are necessary. You are squeezing out the very best of you, and that takes muscle power.

I want you to write a letter to your future nursing self. Not only is this wildly therapeutic, it will help you concretely see your growth when the time comes.

Write down where you are today and the aspirations you have for yourself. Be bold. You'll surprise yourself when you read it again one day and look back at how far you've come.

_____

_____

_____

_____

_____

_____

_____

_____

_____

Afterword

I HOPE THIS BOOK has rejuvenated your soul. I hope on the days you feel depleted, these affirmations replenish you. I wish you sunshine on rainy days. I wish you rain when it feels like a drought. I wish you complete fulfillment and purpose in this ever-so-special career choice. I hope that on the days you feel the most anxious, this book will be your lavender and peppermint tea...